The Development of Agriculture and Forestry in the Tropics

THE
DEVELOPMENT
OF AGRICULTURE AND
FORESTRY IN THE TROPICS

Patterns, Problems, and
Promise

by

JOHN PHILLIPS

Formerly Professor of Botany in the University of Witwatersrand,
Johannesburg, South Africa and of Agriculture in the University
College of Ghana, Legon, Accra
Consultant in Agriculture on various International Bank and
other Economic Survey Missions 1951–9
Chairman, Advisory Committee on African Agricultural Develop-
ment, Ministry of Native Affairs, Southern Rhodesia

FABER AND FABER
24 Russell Square
London

First published in mcmlxi
by Faber and Faber Limited
24 Russell Square London W.C.1
Printed in Great Britain
by Spottiswoode, Ballantyne & Co. Ltd.
London and Colchester

To
my Colleagues on World Bank and other Missions,
through whom I have learned how little I know
of the Tropics and the Hotter Subtropics, I
gratefully subscribe these pages

Contents

9

CONTENTS

CONTENTS

11

CONTENTS

CONTENTS

13

CONTENTS

CONTENTS

15

NOTE

In this book the titles Union of South Africa and Union should be read as the Republic of South Africa.

Preface

In December, 1959, Professor S. Herbert Frankel of Nuffield College, Oxford, an old friend and colleague deeply interested in the economies and ways of life in the tropics, suggested that I should write a short account of the more significant observations I had made during the various World Bank Missions and other forays in representative portions of these great regions.

After discussing the proposal in principle with friends in the World Bank, Professor Frankel and Messrs. Faber and Faber, I considered with care the possible approaches I could make to this varied subject—varied because of the very range of the countries, conditions, problems and human communities embraced. In the end I decided to attempt nothing detailed and highly technical, but rather to draw together within the broad classification of the *patterns*, the *problems* and the *promise* of agriculture and forestry in certain sectors of these regions, the matters I think are of more than ordinary importance in the development of agriculture and forestry. The points selected for discussion should provide scope for criticism from those who are concerned with the stimulation of progress in these still underdeveloped regions.

But the form of narrative I have followed has its limitations: owing to the necessity for brevity in so wide a subject, I have been unable to deal with various matters which some rightly consider as vitally important—for example, details of commodity crops, plantation production, and various patterns of 'shifting cultivation', nomadism, types of indigenous livestock and their 'management', inland fisheries, and land tenure. For these shortcomings I ask forgiveness—perhaps I may have the privilege of dealing with some of these in a later work.

I must make it clear that my own travels have taken me only to Peru, Nicaragua and Costa Rica in Latin America, various countries in Africa and Ceylon and Malaya in Asia: for the rest I have depended upon references in World Bank reports and other literature. I have not included Oceania, notably Australia and New Zealand, because of the special nature of the agriculture, forestry and economics of these important and rapidly developing countries.

PREFACE

For the want of information I have not touched upon the warmer portions of China and adjacent territories.

For encouragement I am grateful to the President of the International Bank for Reconstruction and Development (World Bank), Mr. Eugene R. Black, who kindly read the manuscript, and to Mr. R. H. Demuth, Director, Technical Assitance and Liaison Staff of the Bank, with whom I have discussed the development of agriculture and forestry in the tropics on many an occasion since 1951. I emphasize, however, that none of my opinions necessarily expresses the views of the Bank: they are my own, and for them I alone should receive due censure.

I appreciate sincerely the kindness of Dr. Nkrumah, Prime Minister and, later, President of Ghana, and the Council of the University College of Ghana, for permitting me to serve on International Bank and other Missions.

My thanks are due to my wife for the inspiration she gave me, Mr. and Mrs. P. R. Hill for various kinds of practical assistance, my Secretary, Mr. Charles Adjei-Appiah, who typed the manuscript, Mr. S. J. Smuts, for preparing the map based on my notes, and my colleague, Mr. G. G. Corbett, whose undertaking of so many day-to-day official matters has given me time to write this book. Mr. P. du Sautoy of the Board of Messrs. Faber and Faber and members of the firm's staff have been the spirit of helpfulness throughout.

With sincere appreciation I acknowledge the opportunities of wide travel afforded me at various times during the past twelve years by the World Bank, the Food and Agriculture Organization, the Scientific Council for Africa South of the Sahara (C.S.A.) and the British and other Governments.

To my friends Sir Sydney Caine, Director of the London School of Economics and Political Science, and Professor Frankel I owe a special expression of gratitude for their kindly criticism and encouragement.

JOHN PHILLIPS

University College of Ghana, Legon,
Accra, Ghana, West Africa,
22 July, 1960.

Present Address:
Ministry of Native Affairs,
P.O. Box 8177, Causeway,
Salisbury, Southern Rhodesia.

CHAPTER I

Background, Purpose, Definitions and Scope

Background

Persons of the most diverse range of education, occupation and experience are showing an ever-increasing interest in the general development of the tropics and the more severe subtropics. They include students, businessmen, administrators, politicians and statesmen, and their concerns embrace the scientific, the technological, the economic, the sociological and the political aspects of development in both industry and agriculture and the related activities. It is fair to say that a rising proportion of those interested in the tropics and the hotter subtropics is beginning to show a growing awareness of the necessity for knowing not only the economic and technical challenges but also those springing from the background and the way of life of the local peoples. Certain sectors tend to emphasize the industrial possibilities of these regions, but it is becoming clearer to these as well as to all others desirous of developing these lands that usually very much greater opportunities and concomitant problems are presented by agriculture and, according to the particular country, forestry. And this applies not only to the possibilities of more modern practices in farming and related activities, but also to traditional subsistence and other production by the local cultivators and pastoralists.

From the evidence available and the signs of the times there is certain to be a rapidly accelerating interest in agricultural and related development in the tropics and the lesser-developed and hotter subtropics—and this will be spread over the whole gamut of agriculture and, where applicable and feasible, of forestry. A recent view—that of the National Academy of Science and the International Co-operation Administration (I.C.A.) as expressed in its Report of July 1959 on Research in Agriculture in parts of the tropics of Africa—suggesting that the *humid* and the *dry* tropics alike are the *theoretical* acme of potential *crop* luxuriance may be wishful thinking

19

and over-statement, but nonetheless indicates the new approach to the study of the possibilities of developing the productive capacity of these *bioclimatic* regions.

Political progress—and be it proven as early as may be that this indeed is *progress* and not just a passing promise of national freedom remaining unfulfilled in everyday life—is the fashion of the times, and rightly so. But this must be matched as early as possible by a fair measure of progress in the *economy* and general *welfare* in the countries of the tropics and the hotter subtropics, otherwise political stress is liable if not bound to follow. Political and economic development must be in equilibrium or, at most, in temporary 'disequilibrium' only—in the jargon of some modern economists. Failing such a balance, the hearts, minds and bodies of the peoples of the tropics and hotter subtropics cannot benefit to the degree otherwise possible.

As is readily understandable within certain limits, there is a marked aspiration on the part of the leaders of the underdeveloped or less privileged countries—recently granted *political* freedom—to hasten towards what they envisage to be their *economic* freedom. Nowhere is this aspiration more clearly shown than in the spheres of industry and agricultural development. In this in many respects laudable desire there is a serious risk of hasty, ill-planned policies and inefficient practices inflicting grievous harm to the spirit and the economy of a people. The world is learning that a disaster of a financial kind may be even more devastating psychologically and politically than it is to the national economy. In the very essence of unsound policies and their related operations lurks the virus of failure—because the environment of these policies and operations is unsound ecologically, technologically and financially.

Against a background of personal and other studies in or about a number of countries in the tropics and hotter subtropics of Central and South America, Africa and parts of Asia I attempt to examine the broad nature of the *patterns*, the *problems* and the *promise* of agricultural and related development including, where applicable, forestry. Admittedly this is a venturesome task for any one person: the extent of the field is vast, its nature diverse and the background and experience of any one author necessarily inadequate. Preferably this should be the work of a team with a wide range of regional experience in a number of specialties. But the bringing together of such a goodly group of authorities would involve much difficulty,

20

expense and delay. Because there is a certain virtue in taking time by the forelock, this undertaking is thought to be sufficiently significant—in these days of sincere effort on the part of the more developed countries to raise the standards of life and living in those hitherto given little opportunity to help themselves towards a higher level of development—to warrant running the risk of severe criticism for the attempting of too much in too small a compass by one insufficiently qualified observer.

The very extent of the topics involved in a summary of the problems, the patterns and the promise of agriculture and forestry in so great and so varied a setting demands that there should be a critical selection of those matters held to warrant mention. In this very selection itself there is of course ample scope for criticism.

Wherever possible the material on which my views are based is drawn from my own experience, supplemented by published and other reports to which I have contributed, and also from the literature.

Throughout, the responsibility for statements and proposals is mine and not that of any institution or government directly or otherwise connected with any particular proposition. To the International Bank for Reconstruction and Development, the Food and Agriculture Organization and to various Governments I am indebted for opportunities and privileges, but naturally none of these authorities is responsible for any of the views I express as the outcome of studying the information available about any proposition by any organization in any country mentioned.

Purpose

I do not attempt a treatise on the agriculture, forestry and related industries of the tropics and hotter subtropics, because that would demand a knowledge I do not possess and space I could not command. My objectives rather are these:

I endeavour to co-ordinate the most important aspects of the existing information about the *patterns* in crop production, pastoral and livestock industry, forestry, soil and water conservation and rural sociology and economy; to define some of the more profound and pressing *problems* within these particular fields, and to assess the nature, range and relative values of the *promise* these give. Moreover, I try to define the *ecological matrices* in which are set the *patterns* and the *problems*, influential in conditioning the degree of fulfillment of the *promise* for the satisfactory development of agriculture and forestry.

I also attempt to show that while the race between *over-population* —due in no small measure to the improvement in and the much wider extension of public health and other social services—and the *production of food* may be close-run because of the lack of birth-control by peoples whose tradition, dogma and religion are against contraception,* there nonetheless could be an impressive proportionate increase in the winning of food and related needs were the mind, muscle and spirit of all concerned to work in harmony for the attaining of clearly defined objectives.

In the sphere of planning and operations my objects are to consider certain *principles* basic to the formulating of *suitably integrated national policies* for the developing of agriculture, forestry and related activities; and to suggest the nature and scope of the surveys and other studies, investigations and research, trials and pilot projects requisite to the laying of *foundations of fact* for the formulation of proposed policies and practices.

Finally, I suggest the possible means whereby *technical assistance and financial aid* could be provided for those countries prepared to make an earnest, even if a restricted, contribution towards the development of agriculture and the related industries within their own borders.

Definitions

For the sake of a reasonable measure of precision it is necessary to define the meanings of some terms frequently used in the subsequent discussion.

Although all the concepts concerned are covered in some detail in this book it is convenient to define the terms used, in anticipation of references made to them in the earlier chapters.

* But we are ignorant of the facts. It is said that some African and Asian tribes know what local materials to use as contraceptives. It is interesting that in the draft outline of India's Third Five-year Development Plan provision is made for a further 6400 family planning centres—there are now about 2500. How effective these can be in the light of existing uncertain efficiency of contraceptive methods, and the low standard of mass education, is still to be proved.

22

DEFINITIONS AND SCOPE

The Tropics and the Hotter Subtropics

The Tropics, as understood in the text, embrace both the *equatorial* region and those regions extending polewards thereof to the approximate positions of the Tropics of Cancer and of Capricorn, that is the *tropical* regions of many geographers. As is shown in Chapter III, this conception of the *Tropics* embraces the following *climatic* regions of Köppen (1931) and Köppen and Geiger (1930; 1936) as modified by Finch, Trewartha, Robinson and Hammond (1957) and the very broadly corresponding *bioclimatic* regions of Phillips (1959B):

TABLE I

TROPICS AND HOTTER SUBTROPICS

Finch, Trewartha et al.	*Phillips*
(1) *The Tropics*	
(A) *Tropical Humid Climates*	*Highly Humid, Humid and Other Tropical Forest Bioclimates*
	Highly Humid and Humid Forest
Tropical Wet (Rainforest)	Highly Humid and Humid Forest and
Tropical Wet (Rainforest): of Windward Coastal and Monsoon nature	Humid-subhumid Forest and Humid and Humid-subhumid Montane Forest
Tropical Wet-and-Dry (*Savanna*) *Climates*	*Subhumid Tropical Wooded Savanna*
(Dry season(s) usually in winter for the hemisphere, but occur in summer in some subregions)	(In some instances the equivalent is Mild Subarid Wooded Savanna or even Subarid Wooded Savanna)
(B) *Dry Climates*	*Mild Subarid, Subarid and Arid Tropical Wooded Savanna, Subdesert and Desert, with various transitions*
Semiarid or Steppe: *Tropical*	Subarid and Arid (less often Mild Subarid) Tropical Wooded Savanna and transitions
Arid or Desert: *Tropical*	*Tropical* Subdesert and Desert, and transitions such as Arid Wooded Savanna/Subdesert, Subdesert/Desert

23

TABLE I—*continued*

Finch, Trewartha et al.	Phillips
(2) *The Hotter Subtropics,* as here understood, include the following:	
(B) *Dry Climates*	Subtropical Wooded Savanna, Subdesert and Desert
Semiarid or Steppe: *Subtropical*	Mild subarid, Subarid and Arid *Subtropical* Wooded Savanna and transitions (including *induced* and also *climax* Grassland)
Arid or Desert: *Subtropical*	Subtropical Subdesert and Desert, and transitions such as Arid Wooded Savanna/Subdesert, Subdesert/Desert
(C) *Humid Mesothermal Climates*	Humid and Humid-subhumid Subtropical Forest, Subhumid Wooded Savanna, and Macchia
Dry-summer: *Subtropical* (Mediterranean)	Macchia, Sclerophyllous Scrub; (*Fynbos*: Southern Africa)
Humid *Subtropical* (Warm Summer). Moist all the year or Dry in Winter	Humid and Humid-subhumid *Subtropical* Forest (in places Subhumid Wooded Savanna)
(H) *Undifferentiated Highland Climates* (In humid tropics and subtropics)	Montane Humid and Humid-subhumid Forest, Macchia and Grassland (The forest may be coniferous or broadleafed)

Highly Developed, Semi-developed and Underdeveloped Economies*

While our present interest is not in the *highly developed* economies and to a relatively limited extent only in the *semi-developed*, it is desirable to compare these with the economy of our special concern, the *underdeveloped* countries. Because of the wide range of criteria of importance in describing the various types of economy the details are summarized in Appendix I†. As our emphasis is largely upon

* An excellent paper by Fryer (1958) describes these and other economies.
† Although the classification in Appendix I could be criticized in detail at many points, it does give a broad comparison useful as a basis for discussion.

24

the *underdeveloped* economies in the tropics and hotter subtropics let it be said that these are characterized by a low *per capita* income (very largely under 100 U.S. dollars per annum, but in some instances below 100–200 and 200–300); by a relatively low intake per diem of calories (below 2500) and of nutritionally satisfactory food; by a high proportion of the population engaged in agriculture and related activities—at a relatively low standard of individual productivity; and by health, living and educational standards of a relatively low order. It must be remembered, however, that the criterion of income *per capita* in itself is open to criticism, because this often does not assess the value of subsistence, so difficult to define, nor sundry transactions of exchange and barter. But when taken together with the other lacks and deficiencies, these criteria certainly qualify the underdeveloped countries for the description: the 'have nots' of the earth (American Geographical Society, 1959).

As the term *underdeveloped* is considered not to be in the best taste by some today, the alternative *underprivileged* has been suggested as an alternative. As some parts or aspects of some *highly developed* and many *semi-developed* countries are not only *underdeveloped* but also *undeveloped*, this shyness of some politicians in facing the essential facts in their economies scarcely can be commended.

The Development of Crop, Livestock and Forestry Production in Underdeveloped and Semi-developed Countries

In the sense here implied the *development* of agriculture and forestry covers not only the improvement in technique and practice, essential to the fulfilling of policies of development of particular groups of people in specific districts, but also in practical implementation of the objective of all kinds of projects—great and small—leading to the more satisfactory production of required commodities. These projects may be based wholly or in part on either external or local enterprise or on both, and they may aim at the assuring of appropriate export commodities—crop or animal—or at the raising of the level of national subsistence. While emphasis is upon the development of those natural resources relating to crop, livestock and forest productivity, we should remember that rarely is it possible for development of these kinds of natural resources to be successful unless this be co-ordinated with the various other aspects of development, such as communications, related industries, labour and basic public services.

25

Psychological-Sociological-Economic Background to the Improvement of Agriculture and Forestry in Underdeveloped Lands

From working with farmers and others living near the soil and from the experience of others, I find it abundantly clear that ultimately the success of attempted developments in soil and water conservation and reclamation, the raising of the agricultural productivity of a community, and the establishing and maintaining in sound heart of any form of large-scaled project in crop, livestock or timber production depend upon factors and circumstances beyond the purely scientific, technical, managerial and economic. The understanding of the traditions, attitudes, foibles, idiosyncrasies—call them what the psychologist will—of the local peoples is the first step toward the winning of their hearts, their minds, their confidence and thus the energy of their bodies and the power these can generate. The understanding of the mind of the local people and the learning of how to lead local effort along a well-planned line of approach to the solution of local agricultural and related problems are among the great challenges—and thus among the great opportunities—for agricultural and other extension workers in countries still undeveloped and underdeveloped.

Ecology as Here Understood

Ecology in common understanding is the study of the reciprocal relations of living organisms—plants, animals and man—and their environment (Phillips, 1959B: 36). Within this admittedly very broad definition there is included, by implication, the responses of the *individual* organism and of *aggregations* or *communities* of organisms; the *action* of the factors of the climatic and soil environment upon organisms and the *reciprocal reactions* of organisms upon the environment; and thus logically also the process of successive changes of environment and communities or *succession*, whereby is generated the ecological *development* of *biotic communities*. To Clements (1916 *et seq.*), one-time *doyen* of plant ecologists, largely are due the principles of this conception of ecology and to his memory is due my tribute for his early inspiration of my own studies in ecology. Curtis (1956) has said that the categorical definition of ecology as the study of organisms in relation to their environment is weak because of its very broadness. He considered that 'a more useful operational definition might be . . .: "Ecology is the study of material and energy changes in biotic communities".' 'This definition involves', he said, 'the comparison of *efficiency* of communities in *space* and the changes in efficiency in *time* as the communities develop.' He further claimed that included is the study of the organization of structures, through which energy and materials flow, and of the methods whereby that organization is maintained. If, indeed, all this is inferred in the definition I accept it.

Biotic Equilibrium and Disequilibrium

Various studies in the ecological field both by others (*vide* Chapter VII for references to the literature) and by myself (Phillips, 1930A; 1949; 1959B) have supported Clements's (1916) concept of the living together of plants, animals and man in a *biotic* community, resembling in some respect a *complex or quasi-organism*. Fraser Darling's work outlined in Chapter VII, for example, throws light upon the need for a better understanding of the biotic relations existing in Nature and upon the practical possibilities and difficulties of maintaining these in agriculture, livestock and pastoral farming, forestry, wild life conservation and other forms of development and management of living resources. The disturbances leading to so-called *disequilibrium*, so common in all forms of management not based on a sound appreciation of the ecological setting of any particular project, are still imperfectly understood. Until more knowledge of these and how they may be avoided becomes available, we must expect to make serious mistakes in the management of agricultural and related forms of development, particularly in the underdeveloped countries where our knowledge of local Nature still is sketchy.

Significance of the Concepts of Patterns, Problems and promise in the Investigation of Agriculture and Forestry in the Tropics, Subtropics and Elsewhere

By *patterns* in the arts of crop, livestock and other forms of agricultural production and in the attitudes toward and the management of indigenous forests in underdeveloped countries, I imply the broad *repetition* of phenomena in human behaviour, in field and other practice and in the responses of natural vegetation, climatic and soil factors to particular kinds of practice. By knowing something of the *patterning* of activities and development in certain sets of conditions and circumstances we should be able to improve more readily the production of both subsistence and exchange commodities, simultaneous with the conservation or even the amelioration of the environmental factors.

In like manner there appears to be a fairly broad *recurrence* of special difficulties—of *problems*—in particular settings and patterns. When the relationships, setting and nature of these are better known, we should be capable of finding more effective solutions to these than hitherto.

Man, no matter how primitive he might be, is ever on the alert for features in Nature that appear to offer a reward for whatever exertions he is called upon to make in their examination and exploitation. These features *promise* that in return for certain human sacrifices of time and energy—which often imply money—some return will be forthcoming. To assess more satisfactorily the *promise* of undertakings in farming or in forestry is an objective that every good farmer or forester subconsciously, if not otherwise, sets himself.

Scope and Plan of the Discussion

In outline the scope and plan of the book are thus:

(1) *To examine* the broad nature of the *patterns, problems* and *promise* of agriculture and forestry in the tropics and the hotter subtropics (Chapter II).

(2) *To outline* the major tropical and hotter subtropical bioclimatic regions, on the bases of Finch, Trewartha *et al.* (1957) and Phillips (1959B), and to examine some of the ecological phenomena in these regions, considered to be of special significance in the development of agriculture and forestry (Chapter III).

(3) *To review* successively the *patterns, problems* and promise in:

(i) *Crop production* for subsistence and sale, annual and other (Chapter IV).

(ii) The *Pastoral and livestock* industry, with special reference to production, husbandry and health (Chapter V).

(iii) *Forest conservation and management*—for the purposes of protecting soil and water, the production of timber, pulp and other materials, and a balanced 'small farmer' type of agriculture (Chapter VI).

(4) *To consider:*

(i) Certain essentials to the satisfactory development of agriculture and forestry: such as communications, water, storage, processing and marketing of products, co-operative movements and the like (Chapter VIII).

(ii) Agricultural and related development against the background of policy, planning, research, technical assistance and financial aid—the immensity of the task being emphasized (Chapter IX).

(5) *To draw* general conclusions as to the prospects and problems in the agriculture and forestry of the regions concerned (Chapter IX).

Students of the technical and the economic aspects of development in the tropics and hotter subtropics will appreciate that an attempted coverage of so many topics, in so small a compass, demands a concentration upon important features relevant to the general theme.

CHAPTER II

Some Aspects of the Patterns, Problems and Promise of Agriculture and Forestry in the Tropics and the Hotter Subtropics

I t might be objected that the features mentioned here are hetero-geneous and for this reason scarcely justify being brought to-gether for a related discussion. Actually the very diversity of the matters mentioned by me appears to be an argument in favour of their being drawn together for general consideration. The very fact of their existence is surely the most weighty argument possible for their being studied with as much correlation as possible.

People, Health, Food and Education

The 'population bomb',* as it has been called, is considered by some students of human relations to be more dangerous than the threat of nuclear war (*see* in the Bibliography, the items marked*). The reference is of course to the rising rate of increment in fertility and the reducing rate in mortality, due to improved and much more widely extended public health, medical and other protective social services and to some expansion in depth and spread of elementary and other education. Undoubtedly the threat of the so-called 'explosion' due to an increase in population will continue to be great and imminent in parts of Asia—notably India and China—but must be heeded increasingly in parts of Latin America, the West coast of Africa, the valley of the Nile and in Ruanda Urundi. The problem of local over-population within specific countries of course is no new feature, but will grow in difficulty the longer practical solutions remain unfound or unapplied.

A recent study of the future growth of world and regional popu-lations by the United Nations (1958: 28) reveals the widespread and

* Termed a desperately uncomfortable prospect by Sir Macfarlane Burnet, O.M. (1960).

the pressing nature of the problems of local over-population in portions of the tropics and subtropics. With a world increment of about 1·5 per cent per annum and with regional increments in parts of Latin America, Africa and Asia of 2·4 to 3 per cent and more, the facts certainly throw into strong relief the shape of things to come. Based on this United Nations study, the broad descriptions summarized in Table II indicate the existing and the probable

TABLE II

BROAD DEMOGRAPHIC FEATURES IN THE TROPICS AND HOTTER SUBTROPICS
FERTILITY/MORTALITY RATES

Region	(1) 1950 to 1955	(2) 1975 'low' assumption	(3) 1975 'high' assumption
Central America	high fertility, moderate mortality	no change from (1)	fairly high fertility, moderate mortality
South America tropics mainly	high fertility, moderate mortality	no change from (1)	fairly high fertility, moderate mortality
subtropics mainly Chile, Argentina, Uruguay	moderate fertility, low mortality	no change from (1)	low fertility, low mortality
Africa tropics	high fertility, high mortality	high fertility, high mortality but declining	no change from (1)
N. and S. subtropics	high fertility, mortality high but declining	high fertility, moderate mortality	fairly high fertility, moderate mortality
Asia tropics and sub-tropics	high fertility, mortality high but declining	high fertility, moderate mortality	fairly high fertility, moderate mortality
Australia tropics and sub-tropics	moderate fertility, low mortality	no change from (1)	low fertility, low mortality
For comparison U.K. and W. Europe	low fertility, low mortality	no change from (1)	no change from (1)
U.S.A. and Canada	moderate fertility, low mortality	no change from (1)	low fertility, low mortality

features in 1975 for the regions with which we are concerned. Appendix I, page 182, shows that in underdeveloped countries the attitude towards birth control is still unenlightened.* Above all, the fact is serious and challenging that while the expansion of production of food for man certainly could be much increased and the tempo of

* Some change is noted in India, where family planning centres were included in the Second Five-year Plan and are to be increased in the Third Plan.

such an increase much intensified, that expansion would be on an *arithmetic* basis only, whereas the increment in human mouths is on a *logarithmic*. In varying degree, then, this pressure of population in relation to the food-producing potentialities of the region or of a particular country, and to the possibilities of providing additional nutritional requirements from external sources, is felt now and will be felt increasingly in time throughout much of the tropics and the subtropics.

Health

Compared with a decade ago the possibilities of the tropics and hotter subtropics being converted into healthier habitats for man and his domesticated animals have been enhanced appreciably by the policies and planned actions of the World Health Organization (W.H.O.), strengthened national public health and medical services, the birth and rapid growth of community development and social welfare services and, so far as livestock is concerned, gradually augmented veterinary services, both international and local. But despite all these excellent efforts the health of man and his more significant livestock remains at a much lower standard than is desirable by modern humane, political and economic standards. Even were the splendid aspirations of Manson-Bahr and others regarding the effective control of malaria by 1970 to be realized over the vast expanses of the continental tropics, there still would remain for some decades at least the equally great challenges from malnutrition, fly-borne and other insect-borne and water-borne diseases and, in Africa the very special problems set by human trypanosomiasis, bilharzia and various fevers still diagnosed as 'pyrexias of unknown origin' or G.o.k.: 'God only knows'! A much accelerated and more intensive attack upon the pests and vectors of disease of veterinary interest still would leave unsolved the deeply seated ignorance and inertia of so many of the pastoralists in the *undeveloped*, the *under-developed* and even the *semi-developed* lands, tropical and subtropical.

It must be remembered, also, that personal hygiene and the rigorous application of the principles and practices of veterinary medicine and livestock husbandry to domesticated animals for long must continue to be marked more by their lack than by their application—with of course notable exceptions in diverse countries in the tropics and subtropics. The bearing of this on the health of man needs no emphasis.

32

Food and the best possible use thereof

It is true that the Food and Agriculture Organization (F.A.O.), through its policies and practical demonstrations in many portions of the tropics (until relatively recently other than the African tropics), has stimulated local governments and, in some instances, groups and individuals to attend more consistently and capably to the production of food. Thus to the growing, harvesting, storing, transporting, processing, preparation and balancing of foodstuffs won from crops, livestock and the waters, both marine and fresh, there has been accorded an attention—theoretical and practical—of a range and of a standard never before envisaged even in the rosiest pipe-dreams of administrators and nutritionists. This being so, it might appear irresponsible to state that, varying with the region and the country and of course with the economic standards thereof, there still is a shortage of food: in amount, in availability at a given period and in dietetic value. Malnutrition, therefore, still stalks many a tropical and subtropical territory and common hunger is not by any means confined to catastrophic 'famine' or 'near-famine' seasons.

It is argued by some, of course, that a widely pervading feckless-ness in simple people living on the land is largely responsible for poverty, hunger, delibility, disease and even premature death during the lean months and the especially rigorous years when drought, flood, pest and disease are particularly active. Unquestionably the frequently encountered tendency 'to eat, drink and be merry' during and for some time after harvest is partly the cause of wastage of reserves that would be most valuable in the lean periods. But to this must be added the depleting influences of poor storage, inefficient processing and quite inadequate protection of the food materials from the ravages of rodents, insects, fungi, various other micro-organisms and other agencies of deterioration. The dietician, more-over, is correct in stressing the relatively low standards of prepara-tion of staple foods, their related monotony and consequential wastage.

Notable exceptions there are to all the foregoing strictures on the amount, quality and standards of preservation and preparation of staple foods, but the truth remains that over far too wide an expanse of the tropics and subtropics the local peoples, in one way or another, suffer from the consequences of ignorance, irresponsibility and poverty.

3

Low Standards of Education

Without being tied rigorously to the approaches and the techniques of education as understood in the highly developed lands, and not forgetting that education for life in the wide, undeveloped and underdeveloped spaces of the tropics and subtropics may entail much that is neither understood nor in any way applicable in more developed communities and economies, it remains substantially true that the degree of ignorance of the simplest systematic knowledge of the elements of the environment, the associated plants and animals and man himself is profound. This is no discredit to the demonstrable wealth of local lore about the weather, the soil, the crops, the wild fruits, the local medicines and toxins, the chase, the myths, legends and traditions of man that does exist. It rather emphasizes the inadequacy of this kind of knowledge to explain to the local people the causes, the effects and the underlying principles in life and how these could be applied to human betterment materially and otherwise. In brief, *organized* common sense, the knowledge emergent from scientific study, is wholly lacking and in its place reigns myth, legend and superstition with here and there a veritable gem of factual information won through years of trial, error and success.

How often is it not demonstrable that ignorance of systematically won information, idleness and superstition are the root causes for poverty, fecklessness, subjectivity and obscurantism! Although this linkage and these phenomena of behaviour are by no means absent from the more developed communities wherever these may be found, their predominance is far less evident: the mind is less strongly insulated from the tradition of accumulated, tested knowledge objectively applied. In this setting, therefore, the student of local lore and knowledge and the educationist of the modern day together must work to salve, from local customs and legend, what is worthy of interpretation by and of co-ordination with information won by acknowledged approaches in modern education. To the agriculturist and forester prepared to assist in leading the local peoples toward a more systematic understanding of crop, livestock and forestry productivity, this interpretation and linkage of local knowledge with the introduced should be of outstanding interest and significance.

University education, in itself, does not often give to the usually small proportions of nationals privileged to receive it the spirit, the devotion, the verve and the initiative so greatly required in the

tropics and hotter subtropics. Learning all too frequently is by rote
—consequently, the graduates rarely show the divine sparkle of
originality and leadership. Because of the relatively low numbers of
privileged persons—except locally in India, the Philippines and
elsewhere in Asia and in Latin America—the depressing effect of
these 'lights that failed' is more serious than in highly developed
countries, where university graduates often are more numerous
proportionately.

Cultivation and Animal-holding the Predominant Occupations and Ways of Life

A glance at the information summarized in Appendix I—com-
paring the essential features of the *underdeveloped* lands with those
of the better developed—reminds us that the proportion of people
engaged in agricultural pursuits is relatively very high in the tropics
and subtropics. Details in support of this conclusion are obtainable
from the F.A.O. Yearbooks of Food and Agricultural Statistics
(1959 and earlier). From Appendix I it is also evident that the *per
capita* annual income from the all-pervading industry—agriculture
in one or another of its many forms—is relatively low: often of the
order of less than 50–100 U.S. dollars. Where extensive engagement
in the exploitation of indigenous forests is a local feature—as in
Latin America, parts of West and Central Africa and of India,
Burma and Malaya—the rates of wages earned by local forest
workers, other than those in the more skilled groups, are relatively
low.

Although it is true that 50–100 dollars U.S. may mean very much
more locally than in the United States, and while the estimation of
the *per capita* income in *underdeveloped* communities usually is
subject to the further difficulty of being incapable of assessing correctly what is gained by subsistence, barter and other forms of exchange both by the farming community and by part-time forest
workers, the relatively low value of the figures is a fairly reliable
reflection of the economic status of the particular communities.

Thus we may assume that a predominant proportion of the
population in the agricultural and forestry pursuits in the *underdeveloped* parts of the tropics and subtropics is poorly blessed in
worldly wealth, as estimated by the standards of the more developed
world. From other sources—again a glance at Appendix I gives an

impression—it is known that the productivity of the so-called average cultivator and pastoralist in these regions is relatively low. Partly this is because he may be unskilled, partly because he is not sufficiently nourished and in robust enough health, and partly because his skill—his art indeed—is manual, with no support from implements and tools other than the simplest and the simpler. Mechanization may be appearing in local communities nearer former centres of expatriate activity, but its comparative significance is still largely negligible. Exceptions there are of course in large-scaled undertakings such as the Gezira in the Sudan and on sugar estates in some countries.

Of the way of life of the cultivator and the pastoralist—the former in the forests and the wooded savannas, the latter in the wooded savannas and the subdeserts for the greater part—it is sufficient to say that this is psychologically and sociologically of the deepest importance in the life, standards of living, traditions and home politics of the local peoples. This is repeated wherever the degree of disruption of the ancestral ways of life of the indigenous peoples by colonialism or other influences has not been severe. A binding force responsible for cohesion and security, this way of life serves in some respects as a great family bond, almost as a simple but exceptionally highly efficient trade union and 'friendly society'. Where this is seriously disrupted by local development—as in industrial and mining enterprises and even permanent public works activities in the neighbourhood—the loss of something vital to the very being and welfare of the community concerned often becomes apparent.

To the agriculturist and forester anxious to preserve what is happiest and best in the everyday lives of local communities which he is endeavouring to serve—be he a national or an expatriate—the fact of the existence of this way of life should be of far-reaching significance. Unless he understands it, works with it, helps to foster or to develop it toward something even better, his labours in the interests of greater efficiency well might be in vain.

The pressing challenge of the future is to prove whether anyone, however well intentioned, will be able to retain what is best in this way of life and simultaneously help it toward something more efficient in economic productivity. Here I must confess myself more than a little doubtful about a large measure of widely distributed success because of the dearth of agricultural extension officers with the fire of inspiration in their souls. In some former Colonial territories the local staff often have a long way to go to achieve the standards of devotion of a proportion of expatriate officers.

The Relatively Low Productivity of Agriculture in the Tropics and Subtropics of Underdeveloped Lands

Not unmindful of the view that the theoretical acme of crop productivity is provided by the environment of the humid and dry tropics but rather critical of this being offered as a generalization, I comment briefly on a diverse range of features and circumstances making the practical answer to such a statement far less roseate than the hypothesis:

Low Standard of Subsistence Production

Depending on the local climatic, soil, vegetation and other conditions, the subsistence productivity—whether plant or livestock—often is low: a family is capable of feeding itself and perhaps one more family or several additional families, especially where barter and sale are practicable. Where the conditions are severe, however, or the circumstances of the season unfavourable, a family may be incapable even of feeding itself. Subsistence production frequently wins comparatively poor prices and is subject to many vagaries of demand. In war and post-war periods and during and after famine or very lean seasons the prices usually are more attractive, but fluctuate sharply with supply and demand. This is especially true of the prices for maize, millets, sweet potato, yams, coco-yams and cassava, and is sometimes true of livestock and their products such as hides, skins, ghee and cream. Only locally and occasionally are the standards of subsistence cultivation and livestock-holding even fairly high. Indeed it will take many decades to raise appreciably the levels of productivity and quality in the various forms of subsistence farming.

Crops for Export, Poor Prices and the Need for Diversification

Export commodities are subject to serious fluctuations in world prices where no international control is exercised. During national or international emergencies they may be more steady and at a higher level: this notably has been true of cocoa, coffee, tea, rice, oil seeds and fibres.

TABLE III

EXAMPLES OF INSUFFICIENCY OF DIVERSIFICATION CROP PRODUCTION FOR EXPORT IN TROPICAL/SUBTROPICAL REGIONS OTHER THAN AFRICA AND OCEANIA‡

(Values in millions United States dollars given with percentages)*

Country	Percentage value of total exports of all kinds	Major items of food exports			Total	Major items of non-food exports		Total
		Coffee	*Banana*	*Sugar*			*Forest*	
Mexico						*Sisal, etc.*		
1954	59	*Coffee* 67:55%	17:11%	8:5%	151	*Cotton* 144:91%	6:4%	159
1955	44	74:56%	11: 8%	10:8%	132	159:94%	4:2%	170
1956	84	87:54%	14: 9%	11:7%	162	376:97%	4:1%	387
Nicaragua			*Sesame, etc.*					
1955	90	*Coffee* 28:76%	5:14%		37	*Cotton* 31:89%	*Forest* 3·5:10%	35
1956	88	23:77%	5:17%		30	24:86%	3·3:12%	28
Costa Rica		*Coffee and cocoa*		*Banana, etc.*				
1955	98	43:55%		34:44%	78		*Forest* 0·2:18%	1·1
1956	99	37:58%		27:42%	64		0·3:16%	1·9
Jamaica		*Sugar*	*Cocoa/coffee*	*Banana, etc.*		*Other agric. products*		
1955	68	32:52%	8:13%	18:29%	62	0·2:67%		0·3
1956	66	35:51%	9:13%	20:29%	68	0·2:67%		0·3
Trinidad and Tobago		*Sugar*	*Cocoa/coffee*			*Other agric. products*		
1955	19	18:56%	8:25%		32	0·5:83%		0·6
1956	16	15:56%	7:26%		27	0·6:86%		0·7
British Guiana		*Sugar*				*Rubber*	*Forest*	
1955	67	24:73%			33	0·3:13%	1·9:83%	2·3
1956	65	25:76%			33	0·3:12%	1·3:50%	2·6
Ecuador		*Coffee/cocoa*		*Banana, etc.*			*Forest*	
1955	94	42:51%		37:45%	82		1·0:43%	2·3
1956	95	47:54%		38:44%	87		1·0:42%	2·4

Country	Year		Export (value : %)				Export (value : %)			
Colombia	1955	88	Coffee/cocoa 487:96%			507	Tobacco 2·1:44%	Forest 0·7:15%		4·8
	1956	84	413:92%			448	3·0:65%	1·4:30%		4·6
Peru	1955	48	Sugar 37:73%	Coffee 8:16%		51	Cotton 68:92%			75
	1956	46	33:70%	9:19%		47	67:87%			77
Brazil	1955	95	Coffee/cocoa 961:89%			1081	Cotton 157:56%	Forest 64:23%		278
	1956	92	2273:92%			2465	274:54%	96:19%		503
Argentina	1955	93	Wheat/maize 334:53%			636	natural fibres (mainly wool, cotton) ...			224
	1956	92	290:45%			643	...			225
Burma	1955	93	Rice 170:90%			188	Cotton 8:36%	Rubber 7:32%	Forest 6:27%	22
	1956	93	179:90%			199	11:36%	9:28%	12:38%	32
Ceylon	1955	98	Tea 257:84%	Copra, etc. 34:11%		305	Rubber 74:90%	Other 2·4:3%	Cotton 5·3:6%	82
	1956	92	226:83%	30:11%		273	61:95%	1·9:3%	—	64
Malaya– Singapore	1955	70	Coffee/tea 46:34%	Copra 43:31%	Fruit/veg. 24:18%	137	Rubber 759:97%	Other agric. products 10:1%	Forest 10:1%	781
	1956	63	49:32%	47:31%	28:18%	153	674:91%	11:2%	11:2%	698
Thailand	1955	89	Rice 159:89%	Fruit/veg. 8:4%		179	Rubber 85:70%	Other 16:13%	Forest 17:14%	121
	1956	94	144:82%	8:5%		176	73:67%	11:10%	11:10%	109
Indonesia	1955	69	Sugar 20:12%	Coffee 61:37%	Copra 65:40%	163	Rubber 430:89%	Tobacco 27:6%	Forest 2·4:0·5%	482
	1956	66	19:11%	74:43%	71:41%	173	355:87%	29:7%	1·5:1%	407

* Selected from F.A.O. Yearbook 1957, except for †.
† World Bank Mission Report, 1959.
‡ For Trans-Saharan Africa vide Phillips (1959B: 312).
All figures are rounded to the nearest whole number.

39

PATTERNS, PROBLEMS AND PROMISE

The range of tropical export crops is limited to a comparatively short list of really highly important items in steady demand overseas. This for long has been the cause of uneasiness on the part of administrative and political circles and, understandably, has been the main spring of the desire to *diversify* agricultural and related production.

Based on data derived from statistics published by F.A.O. (1958) and the United States Department of Agriculture Foreign Agricultural Service (1958 *et seq.*), I have shown (Phillips, 1959B: 312) that in Africa South of the Sahara in *ten* of the twenty countries listed, *one* agricultural export produces 50 per cent and more of the income from exports, while in *fifteen* of these as much as 60 per cent and more of such income derives from *two* agricultural commodity exports. By contrast *seven* countries show a fair diversification of export. In Table III (pages 38–39) examples of *insufficiency of diversification in terms of export commodities* are given for the regions other than Africa and Oceania.*

It must be remembered that while poverty in diversification of export commodities may apply to some countries, this does not necessarily mean that there is an insufficiency of range in the crops grown for subsistence and internal trade.

While it is easy enough for the agriculturist to advise, on *technical* grounds, how to further the diversification of production, it is quite another matter for him and the economist to show convincing evidence that such diversification is likely to ensure any appreciable *economic* advantage within a reasonable time. This is well borne out by two examples, Ghana and Malaya. While upwards of twenty crops of some interest economically could be grown in Ghana, none of these—singly, in groups and as a whole—could provide anything approaching even a mediocre substitute for the major agricultural export, cocoa. Malaya, despite being in somewhat easier circumstances because of her comparatively greater diversity—tin, rubber, coconut and oil-palm—actually is no easier to lead toward a satisfactory economic solution of her dependence upon these exports. There are many crops which are *technically* suitable for the country, but their contribution to the *economy* within a reasonable period would be slight.

* Ceylon, Malaya-Singapore, Thailand and Indonesia (*vide* Table III) export several important crop commodities, but still are insufficiently diversified.

Commodity Crops for Export not always Fully Harvested nor Live-stock Sufficiently Utilized

Depending upon the mood and the need of the moment, the local small cultivator may not harvest the whole of his crop. His attitude may be that he has taken as much as he wishes, worked as much as he is prepared to do, and can see no requirement that cannot be met from the income he is to derive from what he already has gathered. Conversely, he may argue wholly correctly that there are no consumer goods locally available on which he would be prepared to spend more money did he possess this. The absence of incentive clearly is a common enough feature in the tropics and more severe subtropics. Examples of the small farmer permitting material of economic value to remain ungarnered are seen in the leaving of cocoa unpicked in Ghana and elsewhere in West Africa, coffee and cotton unharvested in East Africa and rubber stands inadequately tapped in South-East Asia. To change the attitude of the small grower to the simple economy of more efficient harvesting presupposes a marked improvement in general and agricultural-economic education, and also in local marketing propaganda and extension. This will not be achieved quickly.

Commonly in Africa the disposal of livestock and their products —hides, skins, mohair, milk, ghee, cream—is very far from proportionate to the current potentiality. This often arises from traditional conceptions of the prestige reflected through ownership of a large number of livestock, irrespective of their intrinsic value: a larger number of poorer animals being of greater significance socially than a smaller number of better quality. Religious bases also may play a major rôle in withholding potentially saleable animals from the market.

Pests and Diseases in Crops and Livestock

As the introduction and the expansion of modern plant protection is still far behind the minimum of what is requisite in a high proportion of tropical and hotter subtropical countries, it is understandable that pests and diseases deplete harvests both in the field and the so-called storage stages. In almost all the underdeveloped countries in these regions the international organizations and, in some countries, American or British aid in one form or another, have attempted to introduce the preliminaries of plant protection. But the way ahead is still tortuous because of the lack of a sufficiency of education and understanding on the part of the simple local cultivators and those associated with them.

On the animal husbandry and veterinary side very much the same is true: the vectors of disease and disease in manifold form alike are widely spread and cannot be controlled sufficiently effectively on a small scale let alone on a territorial or even more extensive basis. Men, methods and money—all still fall far short of what is essential to the formulation of sound veterinary policies, rigorously supported and enforced by a large enough number of suitably qualified staff at all levels. But it is fair to record that over the range from Central/ South America to South-East Asia there is discernible a slight to a more definite improvement in animal health services. What is less encouraging, however, is the constant reminder that the simple pastoralist learns so slowly the advantages of following modern veterinary guidance. Tradition if not religion often is the basis for inertia and obscurantism.

Another feature all too commonly noted is the weakness of the linkage of sound husbandry, pastoral management and the control of pests and diseases in livestock. Less pronounced in some former British-administered territories than usually encountered elsewhere, this weakness is noticeable more definitely in parts of Central and South America and of Africa and Asia.

Crop Storage, Processing, Transportation and Marketing

This closely related sequence of post-harvest crop production often is characterized by a very marked to a considerable degree of inefficiency. This frequently is traceable to ignorance, inexperience, poverty and inertia on the part of the small cultivator, to an ineffective agricultural extension service, and to a want of money for simple installations and roads. The outcome usually is a heavy loss in quantity and quality of cereals, legumes, oilseeds and root and tuber crops, costing the equivalent of many millions of pounds seasonally, due to the ravages of the climate, rodents, insects, fungi, bacteria and other organisms. It is fair to note that F.A.O., United States and other government influences now are bearing upon this closely interrelated sequence of requirements. But the hem of the problem alone hitherto has been touched.

OF AGRICULTURE AND FORESTRY

Complex Land Tenure

Varying in importance with each country, the tenure of land is of wide significance and unquestionably in many instances is responsible for some of the low agricultural productivity. Emergent from tribal and other local tradition or occasionally the product of promulgations by Colonial and other governments, the tenure of arable and pastoral land frequently is highly involved in terms of custom, law and regulation, written and other. Accordingly the initial planning of farming, as well as the replanning of activities on land for long under agriculture, are faced at almost every turn with obstacles, sometimes so weighty and intricate that few democratically elected governments attempting to remove these would survive at the hustings. Special attention has been paid to a study of tenure in the rural areas of a number of countries from the Americas to South-East Asia by F.A.O., but rarely has this led the local authorities much nearer the solving of their problems. World Bank Missions frequently have considered the impact of tenure on land use reform and general agricultural policy, and have pondered the special problems set by fragmentation through traditional or legal entail. The diversity of the local problems is reflected, for example, in the Bank's reports on Guatemala, Jamaica, British Guiana, Surinam, Peru, Nigeria, Ceylon and Malaya. Meek (1949) has brought together some valuable information about land law and custom in former and present British tropical territories, while the Afrika Institut, Leyden, more recently has paid special attention to the bases and difficulties of tenure in tropical lands.

Communal arable and pastoral land is beset by problems of conservation, improvement and management arising from the psychological situation that what no one man or family has on a secure lien rarely is cherished. If arable land communally owned is difficult to improve, pastoral commonage is even more refractory to weave into a pattern of sound management.

Livestock Husbandry and Production Primitive but Local Animals often Basically Worth Developing

In an appropriate place (*vide* Chapter V, 'Pasturage, Animal Production and Health') some of the special qualities, demerits and problems of livestock in tropical and subtropical lands are outlined. Suffice it to note here that often the *indigenous* or the *naturalized*

43

animals—the latter notably in Central and South America—often provide material worthy of selection, breeding and improved feeding. If this be true of some of the fine naturalized and also more recently introduced cattle and sheep in Latin America it is equally true of the wide range of indigenous cattle, sheep and goats occurring in many countries in Africa and Asia.

A present tendency to dismiss the indigenous and naturalized local livestock as thriftless and to call for 'new livestock' from abroad will not last, because the facts are very largely against it. But this has a delaying effect if not a nuisance value. Ghana along with some other African countries has been told by some that she needs 'new livestock'; actually she possesses some essentially useful indigenous material merely requiring study, selection, breeding, management and systematic feeding, to fit it for much higher productivity. Here as so frequently elsewhere in the tropical-subtropical countries, one of the root causes of local livestock not providing all that inherently they could produce—in quantity and, within a certain range, in quality—is the failure to co-ordinate animal health in policy and in practice with husbandry, management and production of requisite standards.

Animal Products Poorly Processed

Frequently naturally valuable products—hides, skin, mohair, coarse wool, milk, cream, ghee and flesh—are most crudely prepared, stored and transported. They thus gain a low reputation and provide monetary returns far below those that could be obtained were the elements of proper processing, preservation and transportation to be applied consistently. Some beginning in instructing simple farmers and pastoralists in the art of better processing and storage has been made by the F.A.O. and other bodies and by local governments— but locally only, as in parts of Latin America, Africa and India, is much positive change so far evident.

Pasture and Browse Conservation and Management Little Understood

Natural pasturage and browse management is only just beginning to be understood in a few parts of Central and South America, in a very few countries in Africa—such as in the Union,* Southern Rhodesia, Tanganyika and Kenya—but is still almost wholly unknown in practice except on experimental stations in tropical and subtropical India, in Pakistan and in Ceylon. This is not to say that the

* South Africa.

44

traditional art of the *nomadic* and *transhumant* pastoralist is not most impressive in some respects in the *arid* to *subdesert* to *desert* regions of Africa—from the west to the Horn of Africa—but rather to stress the want of a wider-spread tradition of indigenous pasturage and browse.

For psychological reasons springing from tradition and custom, it is most difficult to stimulate an interest on the part of the simple pastoralist in the conservation and improvement of what he considers has been given him as a *birthright*. Indeed this difficulty is met also in certain European farming communities in Latin America and South-Eastern Africa. I have been lectured by some farmers to this effect: 'If the Good Lord had intended our livestock to have better grasses and shrubs, He would have provided them! If He had intended us to "manage" the wild grasses and shrubs, He would have taught us to do this even as He taught us to husband our crops, flocks and herds!'

A recent tendency—in keeping with that mentioned above for livestock—and regrettably engendered by the assertions of otherwise educated laymen, such as sociologists, economists and administrators, is to believe that the tropics and subtropics, and notably in Africa, need 'new' grasses. Until such be forthcoming in sufficient amount, the livestock industry—it is asserted—must languish. In point of fact, while the Latin American tropics now clearly benefit from the introduction of certain African grasses—*Panicum* spp., *Hyparrhenia rufa*, *Digitaria* spp., *Cynodon* spp., *Pennisetum* spp., *Sorghum* spp., *Cenchrus ciliaris* and some others—there exist native grasses worthy of more serious attention than they hitherto have received. Africa herself has little or no need for exotic grasses, having a wealth of material of her own. Asia could gain from appropriate introductions of African species but also possesses indigenous genera and species of value.

Exploitation and Farming in Forest and Wooded Savanna Regions

In the *humid* to *humid-subhumid* to *subhumid* tropics and hotter subtropics the local peoples traditionally have cultivated land and, to a much lesser degree, raised restricted numbers of livestock, principally sheep, goats and poultry, but more rarely cattle. In non-Moslem countries pigs also may be kept in these bioclimatic regions. Some of the most productive forms of arable farming are conducted by simple cultivators in these same regions.

PATTERNS, PROBLEMS AND PROMISE

In parts of Central and South America and highland Africa, farmers of European stock over several decades also have learned to win a living in forest and wooded savanna of various types. While some of the latter have copied or modified the procedure of the local peoples, they for the greater part have tended to farm *in situ*: that is they have worked not on a rotation in *space* but rather on a rotation of *crops*. By contrast the indigenous people from the Americas, through Africa to Asia have followed the pattern of short period cultivation, moving on to adjacent land either virgin or long-rested from cultivation, and returning to the original area on a shorter or longer rotation: say after five to twenty years.

This rotation is *space*, now widely known as 'shifting cultivation', has a lengthy synonymy, among the better-known local terms being *milpa* in the tropics of the Americas, *taungya* in Burma, *chena* in Ceylon, *ladang* in Malaya and *chitimene* in Southern Central Africa. Vast tracts of forest and wooded savanna thus have been worked over and, in some instances, much depreciated if not destroyed in the course of the centuries. Elsewhere the technique followed has done slight if any permanent harm to the soil.

More recently in Central and South America, in the *humid* to *humid-subhumid* regions more particularly, a tendency has grown to open or 'colonize' the forests. To a lesser extent similar interest has been shown in opening more of the forests in Africa and Asia—as in Ceylon, Malaya, Indonesia—to farming. Unless every necessary precaution is taken to plan these new ventures along the lines of sound policies and practices of conservation, the rapid and extensive deterioration of the relatively sensitive forest soils, and thus the productivity of these areas, is inevitable. This deterioration, physical, in nutritional value and in biotic nature is becoming increasingly more common and serious wherever the degree of exposure and the length of the time of subjection of the soil to insolation and direct rain exceed fairly restricted limits.

The creation and the rapid expansion of *derived* or *man-made* (*induced*) wooded savanna and open grassland are becoming more apparent and in many countries, over the whole range of the tropics, in accordance with an increase in population and an accompanying invasion of the forests and wooded savannas. In true wooded savanna in the *subhumid* to *subarid* regions (*vide* Chapter III) an extensive but a less serious deterioration has occurred in the relevant characteristics of the more robust, less readily despoilable soils. Such

46

regions exist mainly in *subhumid* South America, *subhumid* Africa and on old *forest* land and in true savanna in Asia.

Forest Conservation and Management still Relatively Local in Relation to the Development of Agriculture in the Forest Regions Proper

Passing reference has been made above to the forests proper—that is to the *climax* or ultimate vegetation in the *humid* and *humid-subhumid* tropics and subtropics. It is opportune to touch briefly on the increased risk to the existence of a sufficiency of forest for purposes of timber and other production and the conservation of water supplies for the regulation of rivers and streams, inherent in the future 'colonization' of these wooded lands by farmers.

As the subject of forest conservation and management is discussed more fully in Chapter VI it is now necessary only to note that the conservation, management and silvicultural improvement of indigenous forests in most of the tropical and subtropical countries are still comparatively local. Excellent progress has been made in India, Pakistan, Malaya, British West and East Africa—progress which the newly constituted representative governments appear likely to continue. Some equally able work has been accomplished in the former French West and Equatorial Africa and, to a much more limited extent, in the former Belgian Congo. Unfortunately there is still little if any serious effort in Central and South America to study, conserve and manage the forests. With an increased interest by local governments and also by private enterprise in the possibilities of the arable and pastoral development of the *selva* in Central and South America and the *jungle* in South-east Asia, strong and planned efforts to set aside official forest *reserves*—for the controlled exploitation of timber and other products, game, fish and nature conservation—become imperative.

The interrelations of 'shifting cultivation' and the rehabilitation of forest for timber and other economic needs for long have been realized in India, Burma, Malaya and elsewhere in Asia, but require emphasis in Central and South America and Africa. In these latter regions the application of the notable *taungya* method of re-establishment of trees on exploited and farmed forest land is either wholly or almost unknown.

To inculcate a *forestry sense* into the nationals of the better forested tropical countries remains a heavy responsibility for the forestry minded Western nations, but the encouraging results in India, Pakistan, Ceylon, Malaya, Nigeria and Ghana are noteworthy and should be emulated in Central and South America and elsewhere in Asia and Africa.

Soil Erosion and Wastage of Water Common Features

Erosion and other forms of deterioration of soil and the wastage of water are common features in the tropics—especially in the *subhumid*, the *subarid*, the *arid* and the *subdesert* wooded savannas. These phenomena follow arable and pastoral farming in which the elements of soil and water conservation are not observed sufficiently, if at all, in local practice. Although soil deterioration and water wastage are more impressive in the *less humid* regions, it is no exaggeration to say that in the *humid* forests of various types there is sufficient demonstration of these wasteful processes to cause concern. Fertility, physical characteristics and biotic phenomena in both the wooded savanna and the forest bioclimates are being deteriorated by an intensification of feckless cultivation and—more particularly in the wooded savanna—by uncontrolled grazing and browsing. The evanescent nature of the linkage of fertility–physical features–biotic phenomena in the soils of the humid forests is especially disturbing. But this must not be permitted to deflect attention from the losses from certain of the less resistant wooded savanna soils, and even from the deep soils of the subdesert, where local cultivation is possible in the more favoured seasons and where extensive livestock farming is practised.

Accelerated Encroachment by Woody Shrubs and Subshrubs

In the normal processes of plant succession the incoming of woody growth is to be expected throughout the tropics and subtropics, the climax vegetation being either forest or wooded savanna rich in scrub and bush. But man aids the development of woody growth by reducing the competition between grasses and shrubs and subshrubs through the medium of over-stocking and thus over-grazing of the grasses—the favouring of the non-grasses being the outcome. Truly the acceleration and intensification of the encroachment of woody and often thorny growth is becoming a curse in a rapidly expanding proportion of wooded savanna in parts of the Latin American, African and Asian tropics and subtropics. The botanical nature and ecological features of the encroaching growth naturally vary with the continent and the region. The distribution of the problem is from the *subhumid* to the *subdesert* bioclimatic regions. In Africa vast areas in West, East, Central and Southern Africa are being invaded by growth largely useless to livestock because of its being almost impenetrable except by elephant and rhinoceros. The two advantages of the thorny, woody cover are the protection afforded to the soil, during windy and rainy weather, and the provision of an abundance of fuel.

Scarcity and Poor Distribution of Water

In a truly enormous expanse of country of *subhumid* to *subdesert* and *desert* nature the poverty in and the unsatisfactory distribution of water, especially perennial water, restrict the progress of man, his livestock and the possibilities of his augmenting an often unreliable rainfall by supplementary, local irrigation of the simplest kind. In many parts of Africa and of drier Asia the problems of the development of greater supplies of water at more reasonable distances apart are far greater than they are in most portions of Latin America.

But it still is insufficiently understood by many politicians, administrators and even agriculturists and engineers that in the *subhumid* to *subdesert/desert* regions a highly delicate equilibrium exists in relation to the availability and distribution of water, and the risks of inducing either erosion or the intensification of woody growth wherever perennial subterranean or surface water is provided where hitherto little or no water has existed. This is demonstrable, for example, in the drier portions of Central and South America (notably the littoral Peruvian and Chilean subdeserts or *costa* and in the highland *sierra*); in South Africa, the Federation of Rhodesia and Nyasaland, Bechuanaland, parts of Tanganyika, Kenya and the Somali Republic; and in the *subhumid* to *arid* portions of Pakistan and India and even in the 'dry zone' of Ceylon. The necessity for careful planning and detailed local management of drinking points for livestock and of water for irrigation is becoming more apparent. Should satisfactory management be wanting, the last state of the locality is likely to be worse than the first—man and beast are likely to suffer greater hardships even than before.

In the foreseeable future sea and other heavily mineralized water is likely to be de-salted and to be pumpable over lengthy distances, for the purpose of irrigating the more fertile *subdesert* and *desert*

4   49

soils. But the unscientific application of water to such *arid* and *desert* soils readily would spell the loss of land to black alkali or brack, the leaching of nutrients and the rapid spread of sheet and gully erosion.

International and United States technical aid must be more alive to these risks of a disturbed natural balance than hitherto.

Superabundance of Water and High Humidity

In the *highly humid* and *humid* forests and also in the *subhumid* wooded savanna regions of the three continents there occur many examples of the problems presented by excessive moisture. These include: (i) poor aeration, high acidity and retarded drainage of soils and their resultant infertility; (ii) difficulties in the harvesting, processing and storage of crops; and (iii) where humidity and temperature remain at a high level and oscillate only very slightly diurnally and seasonally, the relatively poor condition of livestock and the lower physical vigour and mental alertness in man himself. Such 'hot-house' conditions also encourage pests, parasites and disease in subsistence and other crops, livestock and man.

Poverty in Means of Communication

Depending upon the geographic setting, the topography and the distance from more developed parts of the world, the various means of communication range from very poor to mediocre and rarely to fairly satisfactory. This applies not only to roads of all classes— from main to feeder—but also to railways, ocean or river ports, landing strips and aerodromes, telecommunications and postal services. In rural communities largely dependent upon the sale or any other form of exchange of subsistence products, a scarcity and even an absence locally of feeder roads linking them with main roads and railways have a marked retarding influence. A reflection is the lack of initiative in cultivation; because of the long distances, head-loads must be carried and livestock driven—the second sometimes many scores and even hundreds of miles. Remarkable responses on the part of some rural communities to the provision of feeder roads —either wholly by the central government or partly thereby and partly by communal voluntary labour—have been noted in Africa and elsewhere. This encourages the thought that more concentrated effort to provide these comparatively simple and cheap roads, and to cover their *seasonal maintenance* would stimulate local production.

Power: Its Absence or Poverty

Power for local industries and public and domestic requirements in general is poorly distributed, despite some remarkable examples of locally very high potentiality for its development *hydro-electrically*. Surveys and general impressions support the view that in the *humid* to *subhumid* tropics and subtropics from Latin America to South-East Asia there exist numbers of sites possessing the essential requirements for large to small hydro-electric projects. According to the U.S. Geological Survey (1948) the potential and developed water power of the tropical continents is of the order shown below:

TABLE IV

WATER POWER IN THE TROPICS AND SUBTROPICS
(in million horsepower)

Region	Potential	Developed	Percentage developed
Africa	274*	0·4	0·1
Asia	151	12·1	8·0
South America	67	2·4	3·6
Oceania	20	1·3	6·5

* Recently it has been estimated that the potential for Africa is about 41 per cent of the world capacity: U.N.O. (1956). North America and Europe are estimated to have a potential of no more than 84 and 68 million horsepower respectively.

Obviously these figures are meaningless unless correlated with the distances involved in the hydro-electric power being brought to the requisite sites and with the usage to which this would be put. But they convey some impression of the possibilities of development of this source of power, other factors being satisfactory.

Now that the new vista of large-scaled generation of atomic power has opened up, it is conceivable that the remote places of the tropics and subtropics might be served with power for agricultural and related industrial use within the next half-century. The effect of such a happening should be a great stimulus to local production and processing. Dreams of irrigation by means of *de-salted* water pumped many miles from oceans and salt pans are among the visions of the future.

PATTERNS, PROBLEMS AND PROMISE

Some Human Attitudes in the Tropics and Hotter Subtropics

Although there are other aspects of the inefficiency of agriculture in the regions with which we are concerned, sufficient has been said to support the thesis that this way of life and industry needs stimulation and support.

It is necessary to mention some human attitudes and related matters which bear directly upon the comparative inefficiency of agriculture in these regions.

Correlation between Inadequate and often Otherwise Unsatisfactory Agricultural Education, Extension and Research Services and the Traditional Attitudes to Crop and Livestock Husbandry

As a lead to the subject of some common features in the attitudes of simple cultivators and pastoralists toward the raising of crops and the rearing of livestock, it is desirable to mention the existing inadequacy of demonstration, training and education in the elements of agriculture. Earlier in this Chapter the low standards of general education are noted, but it is stressed simultaneously that there is a fund of local lore that cannot be dismissed. In this belief I now emphasize the beneficial bearing that a sufficiency of satisfactory demonstration, training and simple education and a really practical extension service, backed by local and other relevant research, could have upon the agricultural productivity of simple rural communities.

Obviously the conditions vary widely according to country and even districts but a generalization of fairly wide application is that relatively low standards of demonstration, extension and simple education in crop and animal husbandry and health prevail. The local extension services may endeavour to do all they can to aid, but so often they are short in both number and quality of staff at the various levels and, particularly, in that most important grade, the junior assistant on the ground itself. Injections of American and other technical assistance at the higher levels certainly make for an enhanced efficiency in administration, but do not always produce enough practical improvement in the field, Advisory services frequently fail to understand the intricate interplay of the traditional, the sociological and the economic with the technical aspects of local cultivation and livestock husbandry. The investigation of *ad hoc* problems more often than not is ill supported by staff and other requisites, and accordingly fails to ease the vexations springing from the poor responses and the pests and diseases of staple crops and

52

local livestock. In part this is traceable to a meagre research coverage, but also is due to an unsatisfactory linkage of research with the practical application of its results in the field and the herd.

Some Common Features in Traditional Attitudes

Avoiding detail I can say safely that in many parts of the tropics and hotter subtropics the simple cultivator and pastoralist have inherited—and hold tenaciously—views and attitudes to land, soil, natural vegetation, cropping and the holding of livestock, steeped in legend and tradition or having an interwoven element of superstition. That this should be so is neither novel nor difficult to understand: Western rural communities themselves not so long ago were steeped in myth and superstition. But the realization of this background should be the basis of sympathetic efforts to blend with the traditional beliefs and practices—where these permit of such—the systematic knowledge won by scientific and other objective investigations. To attempt to jettison, prematurely and in hot haste, all that the local peoples believe to be important in their field and animal husbandry would be to court a complete lack of confidence, resulting in a deadlock in efforts exerted to raise the quality of local practice. This may not be understood sufficiently widely and deeply by authorities on extension in the highly developed countries, but the sooner this is heeded by advisers whose sole experience hitherto has been in these countries only, the better.

A point made in my comments elsewhere (Phillips, 1959B: 299) on the education of African University students reading agriculture, applies equally well to young men in many parts of Asia and is not without reference to the local peoples of Central and South America: the necessity for inculcating into educated nationals of tropical and subtropical countries a sense of the dignity of 'clean' dirt in agricultural practice. Dust, mud, blood and oil on the farm do not sully nor should they lower prestige. It is as well to temper any tendency on the part of Westerners to be ultra-critical, with the knowledge that traditional status, caste and religion often are the root causes for the apparently inherent dislike in educated nationals of many underdeveloped countries of engaging in rough, hot, dirty practical field, workshop, byre and livestock port-mortem work. We still have to learn the most acceptable way in which to lead such men to set an example in the interests of the progress of their art and science.

In many countries a group if not a communal and even tribal

union exists for the provision of food, shelter, raiment and other necessary aid, should adversity or other causes result in the enforced dependence of an individual or his family. Commendable as this is in the humanitarian and moral senses, the provision of what virtually is a 'friendly society' type of support unquestionably is responsible for a sapping of self-dependence and initiative. This is therefore, one of the causes of the low standards of effort in agricultural practice in many indigenous and certain naturalized communities. Again, this occurs not only in Africa but also in parts of Asia and Latin America. It is a relationship not likely to be dissolved even when urbanization replaces to a greater degree the traditional way of life in rural communities. But conscious efforts to counteract the less happy aspects of this bond must be made.

An awareness of the existence and the significance of the pervading *biotic equilibrium* or *balance* in Nature, together with an appreciation of the readiness with which *disequilibrium* can be brought about with consequences that may be serious and even disastrous to the agriculture of the community, varies greatly with the local peoples. Judging from examples seen in all the tropical continents, I believe that while some local appreciation of this fundamental relationship exists in some communities, there is nowhere a deeply seated and a widely spread understanding either of the biotic balance or the inevitable dangers following its serious disturbance. Wherever poor cultivation, an absence of conservation of local water resources and an inefficient pasturage control exist there is evidence of either little or no practical expression being given to what perhaps may be understood subconsciously by the local agricultural communities.

What is perhaps even more disquieting is the knowledge that quite a fair proportion of the foreign advisors, supposedly leading the local people toward higher standards of agriculture, themselves show insufficient understanding of the vital nature of the biotic balance. Aspects of this are noted elsewhere and particularly in Chapter VII.

Some Recently Acquired Attitudes in Governing Circles in the Under-developed Countries

Although made in no spirit of criticism I must observe that in some countries, until very recently under a Colonial administration, a patriotic urge has welled up in representative, independent governments to show their own and their people's capacity for development of various kinds and, particularly, in agriculture. This capacity not uncommonly is considered to have been repressed in the past by the then administering powers. It is understandable that the 'new' governments should be anxious to prove their own and their people's ability to do as well as—if not better than—their earlier masters and mentors. There is a tendency, however, to take undue risks, to hasten without sufficient caution and to make serious mistakes in the conception, planning and implementation of agricultural and related projects.

To any consultant well versed in the kinds of propositions put forward by some of the less experienced administrations—from the tropics of America to those of South-East Asia—visions of grandiose and far from viable schemes, great and small, move across the mind like a kaleidoscope of agricultural fantasy. In an endeavour to analyse some of the phenomena and features that decide success or failure in these kinds of undertaking in Africa, I have stressed the dangers inherent in haste, want of survey and pilot studies and the like (Phillips, 1959B: 359). From what I have seen in the other tropics I do not doubt that the broad generalizations made for Africa are in principle as definitely applicable throughout Latin America and Asia.

It is evident that the peoples—or at least the representatives of the peoples—in the tropics and hotter subtropics rightly are learning that the *misery* to which they had become accustomed by long experience *is not inevitable*. Thus there is an upwelling of what has been called a 'revolution of rising expectations', that is a widespread and deep aspiration for the enjoyment of a life less beset by poverty, hunger, ignorance, ill health and premature death. But unfortunately this laudable desire for the better life is not often and sufficiently modified by the realization that there are no short-cuts to the winning of the longed-for opportunity and goal, and that mushroom-like development in agriculture and the related disciplines and industries is highly expensive, fraught with imminent risk and highly vulnerable to disaster. Herein lies the necessity for the closer co-operation of the new administrations and those persons of long experience, prepared to be brutally frank, if need be, about the hazards facing roseate propositions thought up wholly or in part for political purposes.

It is noteworthy that the less experienced administrations tend to mistake the *taking of decisions* about the future course of development and the *planning* thereof for *actual action and achieve-ment*. Curiously the shadow is mistaken for the substance. However forgivable this sublimation might be in newly born administrations, largely inexperienced in the prosecution of the basic detail essential to practical success in any kind of agricultural or related develop-ment, this cannot overcome an awkward fact: It takes time for the new order of politicians and civil servants to appreciate the impera-tive necessity for steady and, may be, even infuriatingly slow laying of the foundations of development propositions of various kinds and particularly those of an agricultural and related nature. A philosophy of *festina lente* still may be the safest guide under certain circumstances in the earlier years.

For some time patriotic fervour will continue to prompt the under-taking of too much, too rapidly and on too meagre a basis of infor-mation and experience—with consequential partial or complete failure. In the view of some experienced foreign administrators, well aware of the pitfalls in specific tropical and hotter subtropical lands, some of the leaders of the 'new' administrations first must learn 'to burn their fingers' in the fires of personal, official and political failure, before they will be brought to realize the fundamental necessity for selecting the *right* proposition for the *right* environment, to be carried out in the *right* way by the *right* men. By this means alone should it be possible to ensure sound planning, consistent attention to detail and daily adherence to ethical and technical principles. Severe as such an attitude might appear, I believe there is much in it that is sound. But, of course, wherever it be feasible to soften the experience of the local administrations without losing the opportunity of imparting a salutary lesson in discretion and judg-ment, it is desirable that the shock be cushioned appropriately. Undue severity breeds lack of confidence and thus delays progress.

In the earlier budgets and in the periodic development plans prepared by the 'new' administrations it quite frequently is clear that an excessive emphasis is placed on the growth of the social services, to the almost inevitable retarding of the productive indus-tries such as agriculture and forestry. As much as 25–30 per cent has been set aside for social services in countries while the productive industries have languished for support. Again this is understandable politically, and also because there is a sincere anxiety to better the lot of the masses as quickly as possible. It is as well to remember that even highly developed countries, such as Britain in fairly recent years, have tended to work far too rapidly toward a 'welfare' state.

Administrations newly in power have found that there is a strong tendency on the part of the public—including the rural communities —to look to the national milch cow, the State, for technical and financial support. Unless watched with care and duly curbed, this growing dependence will induce a condition of 'backbonelessness', should too much largesse in the form of social services and the subsidized furtherance of agriculture be forthcoming.

Grouped with agricultural subsidies of too lavish a nature in a particularly insidious form of 'feather-bedding' is the common political urge to provide financial and other aid for University students aspiring to enter the agricultural, forestry, veterinary and related services. While a modicum of carefully apportioned aid definitely is helpful to both the students and the administration, too much support bears with it a serious risk of irretrievable harm in the blunting of initiative and the sapping of self-reliance. This risk exists from Latin America, through Africa to Asia.

Because of the retarding effect it might have on the development of agriculture, forestry and the related secondary industries, a commonly encountered pattern in underdeveloped countries throughout the tropics is especially significant: a great anxiety for *industrial* development for its own sake. A cement factory, a pulp mill, a fertilizer plant and a meat-canning installation are fashionable among the needs frequently stated by administrations to be of the first importance. But often these are of secondary, tertiary and even of no significance economically. Furthermore, an air line, a shipping service in countries with seaboards and a university are among the often pressed needs of would-be recipient governments. Desirable indeed as some of these might be in principle, it all too commonly can be shown that the existing natural resources, labour availability, proportion of skilled personnel, standards of education of would-be senior officers, and official and private finance are wholly incapable of supporting the propositions.

Expecting technical and financial aid *unconditionally* from outside sources, the requesting governments not infrequently are either unwilling to offer or incapable of making a fair and reasonable contribution toward the funds essential to the development of the proposed project or service. Quite correctly has Oliver Franks (1959) commented—in respect of the volume and nature of finance given underdeveloped lands—that free rein cannot be given to countries aspiring to undertake development, merely because they show desire so to do . . . at the sole cost of foreign resources!

Judging from tendencies growing in parts of all the tropical continents there is a gathering risk that the 'new' as well as some of the older administrations may be tempted to follow *uncritically* the pattern of European and North American agriculture, under ecological conditions and sociological and economic circumstances quite unsuitable. This point should be linked with later comments in this Chapter on the subject of the unsatisfactory standards and the inappropriate professional experience of too many foreign advisers.

Certain other Features bearing on Agricultural and Related Development

On the part of both the grantor governments or agencies and on that of the recipient administrations there is a danger in the tendency to burke the issue that foreign aid—financial and technical—really can be of comparatively restricted nature and short range. Such aid should be subject to constant review as to its form of application, if the finer characteristics of the industry and the capacity of the indigenous peoples are to be developed and nurtured successfully. Sometimes political motives complicate the issue. An extremely delicate operation it will prove to be: to administer bilateral and multilateral assistance so as to ensure the *requisite balance* between the stimulation of the verve and the zeal of the indigenous agricultural communities and the avoiding of a superabundance of help, destined to inhibit self-dependence of the right order.

It is insufficiently realized in political circles in the tropics and hotter subtropics that development of any kind—but very particularly that in agriculture, forestry and the related secondary industries and activities—is a slow and intricate undertaking, liable to fail unless based on experience, vision, sound technology and finance and, of course full integrity on the parts of all concerned. Nature cannot be fooled, however gullible the politicians and the shareholders may be!

Whatever the precise detail for any specific tropical country might be, it is fair to generalize that the amount of technical assistance and financial support for agriculture and forestry is in most instances still slight to negligible. The number, the quality and the tropical experience of the personnel available to advise in the tropics are limited. In like manner the funds provided bilaterally and multilaterally in the form of grants and loans are pitiably small in proportion to what is required over a reasonable period.

Whatever the disadvantages of an austere assistance budget and a restricted number of personnel may be, this is not to suggest that there should be a great and sudden increase in assistance funds even were such forthcoming. It would not be possible to administer the *wise* spending of greatly enhanced amounts at this stage, whatever the position might be toward the end of a decade of experience. But it is not easy to convince the administrations in the tropics that there is self-protection in not having an abundance of financial aid at this juncture.

A veritable plethora of advisers is tending to confuse some of the 'new' administrations and some of the older ones as well.* This springs directly from the point already made that the knowledge and experience of the tropics of so high a proportion of these advisers are restricted and even wanting. Moreover, the quality of the would-be advisers is highly variable.

In this relative inefficiency and in this inexperience of the psychological, sociological and ecological setting of the indigenous peoples of the tropics lies the risk of serious misunderstandings and even loss of confidence on the parts of the rural communities and their governments. Signally important, this matter should be drawn to the attention of the highest authorities in the United States, Britain and other Western countries responsible for extending technical and economic guidance as to the improvement of tropical agriculture and forestry.

Linked with the foregoing matter of the quality and the experience of technical assistance, especially at the field level, is the common dearth of nationals of the tropical and hotter subtropical countries capable of rendering fair to good quality technical and *even* administrative service. I say *even*, because more generally the nationals of the tropical lands tend to show a greater flair for administrative than for technical responsibilities demanding more than ordinary initiative.

Herein exists one of the fundamental requirements in all of the tropical countries—the Latin American States and India not excluded—the training, educating and inspiring of a higher proportion of

* Three Prime Ministers of newly independent states have remarked to me that the upshot of too much advice on one and the same topic usually is that no decision is reached and thus no progress made.

carefully chosen nationals in the art and science of the investigation and the putting into effect of development in agriculture and forestry. This naturally presupposes cadres of administrative, fiscal, managerial, scientific and technical nationals prepared to devote themselves to the service of their country.

Reserved purposely for this late point in this sequence of features of significance in the prospective improvement of agriculture and forestry in the tropics and the hotter subtropics—because of its peculiar importance—is the matter of the *instability of local politics*, so often experienced during the past decade and likely to be just as frequently demonstrated in the next. Unquestionably the effect of such instability, if long continued, inevitably will be the withholding of investment from abroad. As foreign capital almost invariably is a general requisite for all forms of development, its lack—because of a want of confidence in the local political stability—must damage the economy. And agriculture and forestry therefore will be retarded.

CHAPTER III

The Ecological Background to the Development of Agriculture and Forestry in the Tropics and Hotter Subtropics

---

General Ecological Bases

As this is not a treatise on ecology, but rather an attempt to view some of the great challenges and issues of agricultural and forestry development against an ecological background, I confine this discussion of ecological principles to several points of practical significance.

Reverting to my more conservative definition of *ecology* as the study of the reciprocal relations of living organisms—plants, animals and man—and their environment and to Curtis's inclusion of the study of material and energy changes in biotic communities (*vide* Chapter I, p. 26). I need add a few additional thoughts only. *Ecology* is not a science in itself but rather an *approach* to the study of the environment, the individual organisms and the communities associated therewith, the responses of the various forms of life to the environment and the resultant influence of these responses upon that environment.

As our knowledge of *biotic* communities—plants, animals and, where appropriate, man living together in a close co-ordination of co-operation and competition—is still local and relatively meagre only, it is not yet possible to attempt to classify the tropics and sub-tropics into major and lesser *biotic* entities. Because our knowledge of communities of plants is certainly a good deal more extensive, we must use—for many years to come—*plant* communities as *indicators* (Clements, 1920; Phillips, 1928A, 1928B, 1959B) of the prime features of the environment and thus of its broad potentialities for various kinds of crop and livestock and forest management and production.

In order to bring out the fundamental relationship of vegetation and the major climatic factors—humidity, precipitation, radiation (light and heat), wind and evaporating power of the air—I adopt the short-cut device of using a variant of the concept of the *bioclimate*—

in the special sense of this being a complex of climatic conditions controlling the vegetation within a natural region. In this sense a *bioclimatic* region is constituted as the outcome of a certain interplay of climatic factors and biotic phenomena, so integrated as to permit the development of natural vegetation to a stage where this is in *dynamic equilibrium* with the climate. This stage is the *climax* or final expression of the interplay of climatic and biotic phenomena— examples being forest, true grassland, subdesert and desert. Where the development is either retarded or inhibited by some influence— often man-induced—the prevailing temporary bioclimatic unit remains at a point either one stage or any number of stages below the climax: the *subclimax* or *proclimax* respectively (Clements, 1936). A wooded savanna is a common example of such non-climax stages in the tropics and subtropics. But it is important to stress that no serious student of ecology, agriculture and forestry would be prepared to rest the matter of the *indicator* significance of bioclimatic regions, subregions and lesser entities upon *climatic* and *vegetation* phenomena only. He must include the physical, nutrient and biotic factors of the *soil*, because of their fundamental influence in conditioning the precise vegetation community and in determining the potential productivity of a bioclimatic locality.

It is also necessary to remember the existence, in all bioclimatic regions and lesser units, of natural or *primary* plant communities and of those created by man directly or indirectly or by some other influence external to the normal association of the community: the *secondary* or *induced* plant communities. A contrast makes the difference clear: A forest which has developed through all the stages of succession without interference from outside—and notably by man and his influences—is the product of *primary* succession and thus is a *primary* community. A wooded savanna (wooded grassland) or an open grassland brought into being by the disturbance of natural forest—by fire, felling, cultivation or any other practice by any agency external to the community—is a *secondary* community. In parts of the tropics and subtropics really vast areas of *primary* forest, subdesert and desert contrast with very extensive regions of *secondary* wooded savanna and fairly large areas of open or almost open *secondary* grassland. What the *climax* is in some wooded savanna is still unknown, because annually or irregularly fire ravages these great communities in South America, Africa and parts of Asia and thus keeps them in a non-climax or so-called *proclimax* condition.

Terms Used in the Classification of Bioclimatic Regions and their Subdivisions

Some terms used in outlining the major bioclimatic regions in the classification* of the various tropical and subtropical countries, and in discussing the several aspects of agriculture and forestry therein, require definition:

Forest
(highly humid; humid; humid-subhumid; tropical and subtropical; both low and medium elevations and montane)

Evergreen to mixed evergreen and deciduous vegetation 60 to 200 feet high, with the crowns normally touching, overlapping and in stratification so as to form a closed or almost closed canopy; the soils normally with more litter, raw organic matter and incorporated organic matter than any of the less densely and closely canopied vegetation communities; climax but with great areas of secondary communities.

Wooded Savanna
(subhumid; mild subarid; subarid; arid; subdesert; tropical and subtropical; low and medium elevations; highland; montane)

Evergreen in the moister seasons, deciduous or mainly deciduous in the drier; 10 to 60–70 feet high according to humidity, rainfall and other factors; the crowns light and may touch, may almost touch or may be separated by short to long distances ... so as to constitute woodland, open woodland, very open woodland; the trees and shrubs may be spaced singly or in irregular groups ranging from a few to many individuals; grass, short, medium or tall, sparse or dense in volume and basal-area, depending upon the espacement of trees and shrubs, availability of moisture, soils and stage of the plant succession; proclimax or subclimax commonly, occasionally climax.

* *Vide* Appendixes II, III and IV.

Scrub
(subhumid to subdesert according to local climate; low and medium elevations and also highland and montane)

Evergreen, deciduous and mixed woody growth, 6 to 25 feet high, often closely intertwined, but may occur in the form of irregular groups or patches separated by open grass glades of varying proportion; the luxuriance depends upon humidity, rainfall and soils; climax where not disturbed; in many localities the climax form of wooded savanna.

Subdesert
(in subdesert to desert/ subdesert climates; also transitional to arid wooded savanna; *Karoo* subdesert is a special subtropical type in South and South-West Africa)

Evergreen, deciduous and mixed stunted woody growth (below 1 foot to about 10 feet); shrubs, subshrubs and brush; may be wholly or partially succulent or sub-succulent or wholly or largely without succulence; spinose in varying proportion, but also without spines; vegetation may be very widely espaced with much bare or almost bare soil, gravel and rock, or may be more closely associated; grasses absent to rare to locally frequent and may even form open communities; climax normally, but often much disturbed locally and in secondary stages.

Desert
(in Desert climates, transition as to *Subdesert*)

Evergreen, deciduous and mixed stunted (below 1 foot, up to 5 to 10 feet) woody growth: shrubs, subshrubs, brush—or vegetation, very, very sparse to absent; sand, gravel, rock may form major portion of general scenery, with local very open to open stunted to prostrate vegetation; grasses absent to very local, in very open communities; oases of taller growth where telluric water exists; climax normally, but local examples of disturbed desert exist, especially when transitional to subdesert.

Mangrove	Littoral and estuarine woody growth 10 to 50 feet high, closed to open canopied, periodically inundated by marine or saline water; tropical, rarely hotter subtropical; conditioned by soil characteristics.
Grassland	Perennial grasses predominant, with admixture of annual and perennial herbs and subshrubs; short, medium to medium-tall; locally tall (over 10 to 12 feet); *rarely climax* (except where winter cold is severe or arid or subdesert conditions hold), *much more often secondary*, following fire, felling, cultivation, heavy stocking by domesticated animals; secondary to forest (humid to highly humid regions) or to wooded savanna (subhumid to subdesert regions); low to medium elevations; also highland to subalpine, where grassland may be climax due to cold: 6000 to 15,000 feet.
	In addition some terms such as *swamp, riverine, flood plain* and *dune* are used in the commonly understood sense.

Symbols Used in the Classification of Bioclimatic Regions and their Subdivisions

For brevity the following symbols are used in describing the *bioclimatic regions*:

Relating to Forest: F
  Humidity (seasonal distribution of rain, vapour pressure, saturation deficit)

      HH: highly humid
      H: humid
      HS: humid-subhumid
      M: montane

Relating to Wooded Savanna: WS
  and *Open Grassland:* OG
  SH: subhumid
  MSA: mild subarid
  SA: subarid
  A: arid
  SD: subdesert

Relating to Subdesert: SD
  and *Desert:* D
  A/SD: arid to subdesert
  SD/D: subdesert to desert

General Basis of Classification of Bioclimatic Regions

This is no occasion for a discussion of the origin and development of concepts of climatic and ecological classification of the major regions of the tropical-subtropical world, but it is necessary to mention several systems that have been of value in leading me toward the selection of a modified bioclimatic basis for the classification firstly of Africa south of the Sahara (*vide* Phillips, 1959B) and now of the tropics and hotter subtropics generally. The first is that of Köppen (1931) and Köppen and Geiger (1936), the second, Thornthwaite's (1933; 1948), and the third that of Finch, Trewartha, Robinson and Hammond (1957). The last is a simplified and otherwise modified version of Köppen's widely known quantitative system for the definition of the broad boundaries of the climatic groups and types. I have found it convenient to use this version for comparison with the bioclimatic classification which I myself have extended from Africa South of the Sahara to the tropics and hotter subtropics covered here. A rough comparison of the major regions which concern us is given in Appendix II.

Significance of the Ecological Setting of Agriculture and Forestry

It has been objected by some—largely others than students of plant, animal, general or applied ecology—that ecologists have erred in thinking too much about the so-called biotic balance or *equilibrium* in Nature and have not concerned themselves sufficiently with the important matter of *disequilibrium* or what occurs when that balance is disturbed (*vide:* contributors to the symposium report edited by W. L. Thomas *et al.*, 1956). Such criticism is unfair when the numerous comments by leading ecologists in the tropics and subtropics about the consequences—evil and other—of the disturbance of natural equilibrium are considered. These cover the whole gamut of activities from the exploitation of forest and 'shifting cultivation' at the one end to the irrigation of subdesert and desert areas at the other. Without going any further than referring to the contributions made to that same symposium by a notable student of wild life conservation and management, Fraser Darling (1956), it would be easy to refute the generalizations made. The point is mentioned because throughout I make reference to the influences upon local climates, soils and biotic communities of the activities of man in his cultivation, livestock management and exploitation of forest. I have tried to do this elsewhere for Trans-Saharan Africa (Phillips, 1959B).

Another point made at the symposium was the capacity for man to *alter* the ecological setting for his activities as cultivator and livestock owner. Moreover, it was noted that the particular cultures of the human communities concerned had differential effects upon the resultant ecological picture or landscape thus *induced*. My comments are:

Broadly, man is compelled to fit his particular form of cultivation, livestock keeping and soil and water conservation—let alone his forestry—into the ecological setting: the bioclimatic and, to a varying extent, the soil characteristics of the bioclimatic unit concerned. But to some degree in the past he has been and probably to a much greater degree in the future he will be capable of overcoming Nature's controls of climate, vegetation, fauna both large and microscopic and soils within *relatively restricted limits*.

Several examples suffice to illustrate the possibilities of this overcoming of ecological controls: (1) The irrigation of great areas of subdesert and desert land by means of de-salted water pumped great distances from the oceans by means of atomic or other highly potent energy. (2) The making of rain over the less humid regions by means at present barely envisaged—for example by means of sound waves* or radiation. (3) The conversion of much present-day 'broken' highly humid and humid forest, in which 'shifting cultivation' prevails, to man-made savanna, with consequent changes in micro-climatic,

* As claimed by the Russians, May, 1960.

soil and biotic phenomena and the probable application of mechanized methods of cultivation. (4) The amelioration of aerial conditions
and health for high-producing dairy stock in the highly humid tropics
—by means of extensive air-conditioning of holding sheds, byres
and dairies.

The notable geographer Gourou (1956)—at the symposium already
mentioned—has suggested that in a setting of physical controls the
'possibilities are more and more in man than Nature'. I agree that
the possibilities are more in man, but only within definitely restricted
limits relative to certain aspects of the art and science of agriculture,
forestry and related activities. Apart from special and local exceptions, man must come to terms with his ecological environment—
hence my interest in relating the patterns, the problems and the
promise of the tropics and the hotter subtropics to the bioclimatic
regions and subdivisions thereof.

The Ecological Approach

I observed earlier that *ecology* is an approach to the collection of
information about a range of matters of importance to the student
of life in relation to its environment. The implication of the *ecological*
approach is that patterns, problems and promise in pure and applied
biology—which includes agriculture and forestry—should be examined as to their interrelations, and that reliance should not be
placed upon merely *ad hoc* interpretations and actions for the obtaining of solutions. I have likened elsewhere the *ecological approach*
to Smuts' (1926) *holistic approach*: whereby effort is exerted to see
matters in relation one to another—to see a problem and a solution
thereof as a *whole* (Phillips, 1930A; 1932). At all events I have endeavoured to think *ecologically* . . . and thus, I hope *holistically*,
about what I have tried to bring together here.

*The Major Bioclimatic Regions of the Tropics and the Hotter Sub-
tropics: Latin American, African, Asian, according to the Classifications of Finch, Trewartha et al., (1957) and Phillips, (1959B)*

For the sake of summarizing the broad *bioclimatic* setting of a
number of countries in the tropics and the hotter subtropics I list
in Appendix IV the comparative descriptions of the American
authors and myself. In Appendixes II and IV the two classifications

naturally do not always correspond, simply because my interpretation of the *bioclimatic* conditions in specific instances differs from that of the other authors. Such divergence usually is due to my emphasis upon some *biotic* feature that might appear of less significance to the geographer.

CHAPTER IV

Crop Production in the Tropics and Hotter Subtropics

Background: Why Crop Production is discussed apart from Livestock

Why, it may be asked, is the discussion about the production of crops separated from that about livestock? Because while there is some semblance of what is known as 'mixed'* farming—that is the farming of crops and animals in varying proportions by smallholders, larger farmers and estates—in some parts of the tropics and to a somewhat greater extent in the hotter subtropics, it is much commoner for the small cultivators to possess little or no livestock of any importance. This does not exclude the possessing of a few sheep, goats and poultry and, in non-Moslem countries, pigs—which may or may not be of some slight domestic and barter significance, but rarely of much commercial value. Conversely, tribes or smaller communities, mainly pastoral, may take an occasional and rather casual crop of millet or sorghum or maintain a reserve of cassava (*Manihot*), but attend primarily to the running of flocks or herds. In the forest regions—especially in the highly humid type (HHF)—these distinctions are clearest because the environment is much less favourable to the larger livestock than is that of the wooded savannas (SHWS, MSAWS, SAWS and AWS) and, under certain circumstances, even the milder subdesert (SD). This is reversed, of course, in the more arid regions, where the environment is much less favourable to crops than the highly humid and the humid forest.

More scientific and progressive farming could counteract in some measure the rigours of the dampness of the forest regions on the one

---

* Because of the relatively low incidence in the *tropics* of 'mixed' farming so commonly practised in the *temperate* countries and in some of the more climatically favoured semi-developed *subtropical* ones, it must be stressed that *climatic* control has influenced the local peoples to farm with either livestock or crops—and rarely and locally, only, with both. This ecological adjustment to the environment has become 'fixed' and traditional in the course of time.

70

hand and those of aridity in the drier wooded savannas on the other, but the economy of this probably would not be viable except under especially favourable circumstances.

Patterns

Considering the large expanses of humid forest and the even greater ones of the highly humid, the vast ones of the subhumid wooded savanna, together with the more promising portions of the mild subarid wooded savanna and the subarid, the small total area and proportion of land so far under cultivation in the tropics are impressive. But despite this comparatively restricted usage of potentially usable land in the tropical-hotter subtropical regions, local land hunger does exist in India, Pakistan and in South-East Asia, in parts of Africa and of South America.

Land hunger is a serious challenge locally to administrations and the people, but over wider expanses there is still sufficiency of soil suitable for subsistence and other cropping by means of both 'shifting cultivation' and 'settled' farming. But the present pattern cannot last for long in some of the more heavily populated countries and districts, and within a decade to a century will have altered also in much of the remainder of the now still underdeveloped countries.

Apart from the population increment a feature that will accelerate this change is the probably relatively high proportion of land that is unsuitable for cropping—and perhaps for long or for ever must remain so. These include areas of much broken topography; very shallow soils of highly erodible nature, high salinity and poor drainage not congenial even for swamp crops such as rice and jute; soils of very low fertility; and of types of vegetation rendering even their partial and temporary control highly expensive of human energy and of money.

Subsistence Cropping much more Extensive than Commodity Production

Of the total area under cultivation at any one time in the tropics and the hotter subtropics the overwhelming proportion is devoted to the winning of crops for subsistence and local barter and sale. The proportion devoted to the growing of commodity crops for export, and also for a restricted local market, is relatively small over all, even if seemingly large locally. Thus for example, *rubber* looms large

CROP PRODUCTION IN THE TROPICS

in Malaya, Indonesia, Thailand and Ceylon; *coffee* large in Brazil, Colombia, the former French West Africa, Angola, Uganda and Madagascar; *cocoa* large in Ghana, Brazil, Nigeria and the former French West Africa; *cane sugar*, for export, large in Cuba, Hawaii and the Dominican Republic; *rice*, for export, large in Burma and Thailand; *tea* large in India, Ceylon and Indonesia; *coconut* products, for export, large in the Philippines, Indonesia, Malaya–Singapore and Ceylon; *bananas*, for export, large in Ecuador, Honduras, Costa Rica, Panama and Brazil; *groundnuts*, for export, large in Nigeria and the former French West Africa; *sisal* large in Tanganyika, Mexico, Kenya and Brazil; *jute* large in India and Pakistan; *pepper* (*Piper*) large in Southern India and South-East Asia; *maize*, for export, large in Argentina and South Africa; *tobacco* large in the Federation of Rhodesia–Nyasaland and India; and, of course, great areas of *cotton*, for overseas or other export, large in Asia, Latin America, Uganda, the former Belgian* Congo and the Sudan.

By contrast, the subsistence crops, or rather those that are used either wholly for subsistence or for subsistence and also for some export, are produced over very much larger total areas, but on a vast number of petty plots of divers shapes. This applies particularly to the staple cereals such as *rice*—notably in India, Indonesia, Burma, the Philippines, Brazil and French West Africa; *maize*—as in Brazil, India, South Africa, Indonesia, Argentina, the Philippines and Colombia; the various *millets* and *sorghums*; the sundry *pulses* and *groundnuts; cassava, yams and taro†; plantains*, sundry other fruits and vegetables. African *oil-palm* (*Elaeis*) is in a special class: indigenous and thus largely gathered for export and subsistence from wild or semi-wild or usually rather casually planted palms in West Africa, but grown mainly for export in well-managed plantations in Indonesia and Malaya.

Low Efficiency of Production Generally

The efficiency of production—that is the amount and quality of the yield per unit area or man-unit of time—is relatively low for most of the subsistence crops grown by the indigenous, naturalized and other small cultivators. Some of the reasons for this are noted later. There are local exceptions to this, of course, depending upon

* Name retained for convenient reference.
† Coco-yam: *Colocasia* and *Xanthosoma*.

72

the circumstances of the locality, the attitude and the capacity of the cultivators and the quality and spread of the guidance given them by the local extension services.

In comparison, the efficiency of the production of the commodity crops is usually higher where foreign or national enterprise is responsible for the organizing of the establishment, management and general administration of the producing areas. This commonly is in the form of well-established and managed plantations, with associated processing installations, transport and perhaps special training of the junior staff, artisans and labour.

Commodity crops extensively produced by small cultivators include: *groundnuts* (in Asia, Africa, Latin America); *cocoa* (West Africa, Latin America); *coffee* (East and West Africa); *tea* (small-holdings and more recently subdivided estates in India, Ceylon and Indonesia); *rubber* (Malaya, Indonesia and Ceylon); *coconuts* (small-holders the principal producers in the Philippines, Indonesia, Ceylon, India and Malaya); and *tobacco* (India, Indonesia, Nigeria and French West Africa). But the yield per unit area and the quality of the commodity often fall below what consistent effort and better organization common on large estates are able to achieve.

It is claimed by Wickizer (1960), in an able study of the smallholder in tropical export-crop production, that copra and cocoa are the most important examples of production for export of major crops by small-farming methods—the exportable products being fairly near the raw state. Any one acquainted with the growing, maintenance and management of these export crops will know how far below the possible are the yields and quality of the harvests. As about 5 to 10 per cent only of the world's cocoa derives from other than small growers and as the proportion of plantation-produced copra is also relatively small, the probable immense loss to the growers, the countries and to the industries concerned is obvious.

If *copra* and *cocoa* are thought to be pre-eminently suited to the small grower, *tea* and *sisal* are examples of crops far less suitable. This partly is due to the expensive capital equipment required for processing and partly because of the skill involved in attaining a satisfactory quality of product for competitive and critical buyers. The growing, the protection, the transporting, and the processing of sugar also demand a plantation and milling organization within reasonable distance, otherwise the small grower could make no use of his cane. The *banana* differs in detail but is dependent upon an

73

estate organization for protection against pest and disease, and for transportation inland and overseas; the small grower lacking the necessary support therefore could not export his produce.

'Shifting Cultivation'

'Shifting cultivation'—mentioned also in Chapter II—is a widespread practice both in forest and in the less arid wooded savanna (such as the subhumid to the more favoured parts of the subarid) and has evolved in all the continents. Existing in seemingly endless variations according to locality and people, this practice possesses some marked virtues and some definite weaknesses. Its outstanding virtue is that it saves soil from severe deterioration, its main weakness that it cannot impart a sense of stability and thus of the value of trying to improve the areas only periodically occupied. But it is unwise to attempt to prevent this practice or to persuade cultivators against it until some other procedure has been demonstrated as more efficient, less potentially dangerous to vulnerable soils when its rotation period is short, and at the same time suitable for introduction into relatively simple communities.

Where sufficient land is available in proportion to the population for, say, the next twenty-five to one hundred years, the opportunity exists for an improvement in the practice and for its ultimate substitution by an acceptable *sedentary* form of cultivation. Where these conditions are wanting, however, a shortage of land and a high increment in population must reduce the period of rest and therefore must accelerate the coming of an *enforced sedentary* practice, which could be most harmful to the soil.

Serious problems naturally are presented also by the related aftermath of still further spoliation through the fragmenting of the patches of land farmed on a *sedentary* basis. This variant of a new pattern is likely to be much commoner during the next fifty years.

Gourou (1956) may be correct in asserting that 'shifting cultivation' is not an essential in the tropics but rather 'an expression of a stage of civilization', but it also is true that this practice originated in the most diverse conditions in the tropics and subtropics and is still widespread. It is academic, therefore, to rail against shifting cultivation unless a substitute acceptable to the simple cultivator and also economically viable can be found. 'Sedentary cultivation' obviously presents many difficulties: indeed it shares with 'shifting cultivation' a common pattern of unhappy experiences in soil spoliation. But let us hope that the promising results so far indicated on a relatively small scale in Southern Rhodesia and Kenya, under skilled European direction, may be the forerunner of greater success in the years ahead.

Where a sound agricultural sense has been introduced by foreigners or by nationals into the cultivation of *commodity* crops, the yields and quality have been more satisfactory than where the unaided local people have attempted to produce these crops.* Almost all of these examples owe their efficiency to sound selection of the commodity crop and a given locality, sensible planning, experienced management and fairly acute business sense and, of course, satisfactory technical knowledge. Should these qualities be lacking among the local people they must be provided temporarily by foreigners, but there is no reason why well chosen nationals should not learn these arts within a reasonable space. (*Vide* Nye & Greenland (1960) on 'shifting cultivation'.)

Low Efficiency of Subsistence Cropping: Twelve Reasons

By contrast the efficiency of subsistence crop production is low, hence poverty and malnutrition are commoner locally than the gross luxuriance in the tropics—even in the subarid regions thereof— might lead one to expect. Among the reasons for this low efficiency are these:

(1) A surprising ignorance of the husbandry of crops prevails in many countries, hence the best possible results are not achieved under the existing circumstances of climate, soil and varieties. Moreover, the great proportion of small cultivators adopts a conservative attitude toward improved methods and new varieties. This naturally varies much with country, district, tribe and community. In some instances excellent responses are made to practical demonstrations on the cultivator's own patch of 'shifting cultivation', whereas in some countries little if any interest may be shown in demonstrations on government land or an experiment station. One of the reasons alleged for the failure of the Second Development Plan in India has been the difficulty of inducing the cultivators to adopt, sufficiently fast, the techniques essential on land under irrigation. Whether a greater success will be achieved under the Third Plan depends upon a greatly improved extension service.

* Cocoa production in West Africa is an example: expatriate guidance is likely to raise the yield per tree appreciably.

(2) Poor seed, due to inefficient selection or to the lack of the simplest facilities for storage and protection against weather, vermin, pests and disease, commonly causes depressed yields. Simple in principle as is the improving of this technique, its application in practice is not easy in the absence of a will for self-help on the part of the people and a vigorous extension service.

(3) Inefficient tools and implements retard progress. Given attention by the Germans in East and West Africa at the turn of the century, this want of good but very simple manual equipment has been reduced only very slowly in many parts of Africa, because of the conservative attitude of many cultivators toward anything novel. Where animal-drawn implements—for ploughing, harrowing and cultivating—have come into use these often are not maintained adequately and hence cannot effect the best tillage. Where there is the beginning of mechanization—tractors and attachments for ploughing, harrowing and cultivation—it often happens that unless informed and practically experienced supervision, usually by foreigners, be available, the machinery is not serviced and repaired as required, with its consequent early deterioration.

(4) The simpler techniques of conservation of soil and water are rarely applied in some countries and not at all in most. It would be unfair, however, not to mention that some simple cultivators in all three continents locally attempt fairly effective means of saving soil and water, and that the progressive farming communities in parts of Latin America, Central, East and South Africa and in parts of India show a good understanding both technically and economically of the need for conservation and of its techniques.

(5) Unsatisfactory drainage and the want of understanding and of means for the control of floods—where irrigation is widely practised by simple cultivators—are responsible for heavy losses in yield: poor drainage acting continuously but the floods causing havoc sporadically.

The extensive improvement of drainage and control of floods may be most costly as well as technically difficult and thus may demand national or even international attention. On the other hand, locally poor drainage frequently could be counteracted by fairly simple precautions, such as the preparation of suitably aligned and graded cambered beds or broadlands (*vide* Hill, 1960), provided either ordinary animal-drawn or mechanically operated ploughs and some practical technical guidance are available.

(6) Excessive irrigation, with consequent wastage of water and

ultimate detriment to the soil, is a common occurrence in the three continents, even on irrigable land long since worked by small cultivators. Even on estates under more progressive management, national or foreign, there quite commonly is a wastage of irrigation water with its well-known concomitants: a development of acidity or of alkilinity (brack) and a consequential decrease in fertility.

(7) Losses in fertility and deterioration in the physical and biotic characteristics of the soils occur in the forest, the wooded savanna and the subdesert regions wherever these have been maltreated or seriously neglected: leaching, erosion and compaction being a common outcome of poor crop and soil husbandry.

(8) In some countries—and these exist in all the continents concerned—poor land-use is responsible for much destruction of the soil and thus for reduced yields. Common errors include the establishment of seasonal crops on steep slopes, to run the cultivation furrows with the slope and to fail to provide against the accelerated flow of water therefrom. Other common forms of destructive land usage are the cultivation of drainage lines and water-conserving vegetation sponges, and the removal or serious reduction of protective vegetation from the eyes of springs and along the courses of streams and rivers.

Occasional examples of fairly reasonable to even wise land usage are seen among simple cultivators in the three continents, but unfortunately the greater proportion shows little understanding of the principles that should guide the selection of arable land. But this must be remembered: the simple cultivator frequently shows an acute awareness of the qualities of local soils for his particular like of production, emergent from tradition and nutrured by practical experience.

(9) Where 'shifting cultivation' no longer is feasible or where the cultivators have been persuaded to 'settle', that is, become *sedentary* farmers, insufficient use is made either of organic manures such as dung, compost, dry litter and green soiling crops or chemical fertilizers.

In the wooded savanna and grassland regions the organic matter of the soils commonly is inherently low due to climatic factors— such as high temperatures, low humidity, intense sunshine over long periods—and consequently a high evaporation—and to annual or other fires. Where wood is scarce or unobtainable livestock droppings are collected for fuel, and so even this admittedly very restricted source of organic matter is lost to the soil. Chemical fertilizers still are expensive, unless manufactured within reasonable distance or heavily subsidized, and the wise usage of these still is unknown to more than a very small proportion of the simple cultivators. Unfortunately all this leads to reduced fertility and unsatisfactory physical characteristics in the soil and to serious poverty in those who attempt to 'settle'. Much more suitably balanced fertilizer at a greatly reduced price and utilized in an intelligent manner would assist in altering this unhappy situation.*

(10) Where 'sedentary cultivation' is practised on small areas— sometimes not large enough to support more than one family on a subsistence basis and only rarely capable of supporting two to three families—crop rotation is conducted inadequately. Not only does this spring from the very small areas—from one acre to several acres to perhaps a score—but also from the traditional acceptability of say one crop or several staple crops only. Thus rice is the sole important staple accepted in one area, sorghum in another, millet elsewhere, and maize in a fourth . . . with a pulse or 'root' (cassava, taro, yams, sweet potato and so forth) where climatic and soil conditions permit. Innovations in the pattern of food crops frequently are unacceptable, except perhaps during serious famine or under other special circumstances and then, usually, only after a clear demonstration of the attractions of the newly introduced crop. Hitherto extension services have not been imaginative in demonstrating the domestic and economic advantages of new crops.

In a somewhat different sense, however, there is a simple pattern of what in effect approaches a rotation . . . through mixed cultures: cereals, legumes, 'roots' and spinach-supplying weeds on one and the same patch of land. This seemingly casual and 'untidy' cultivation has in it the vital germ of good field husbandry, because the mixed cultures maintain the fertility and the physico-biotic characteristics of the soil in much better heart than could single species. These 'untidy' mixed cultures still are criticized by observers accustomed to the 'tidy', clean cultivation of single kinds of crops in the temperate regions. This appreciation of the soil-improving influences of wood and other plant communities in forest and elsewhere actually is part of the traditional lore of simple cultivators in the three continents. It is precious and must not be lost.

* The providing of very much cheaper fertilizers for widespread but intelligent use in the underdeveloped continents would be a splendid gift by industry, and could revolutionize crop and livestock production within decades.

(11) Communal tenure of arable and related grazing areas, a frequent feature in much of Africa and not uncommon in other tropical-subtropical continents, keeps arable farming in a static condition because little if any incentive is engendered in the cultivator. Where the fragmentation of communally held patches of cultivation follows, as in the vicinity of urban areas or on originally highly productive soils, this brings out yet other unhappy aspects of communal tenure. Unless the farming thereon is highly intensive and of good quality, the deterioration of yields occurs very rapidly. This is particularly marked where the local tribal or other authorities have no further land to allocate on a communal or any other basis— as in parts of Latin America, Africa, India and South-East Asia. Inevitably this leads either to grandiose ideas of large-scale irrigation or to the removal of a proportion of the population to forest or wooded savanna, perhaps at a considerable distance and in regions still little explored. An example is seen in the thought in political and other circles that the dense population in the *sierra* of Peru might in part be moved to the hot humid *selva* of the Amazon region, to 'colonize' these verdant wildernesses.

(12) As mentioned in Chapter II, crops in the field and their products suffer alike from pests, parasites, disease and vermin. Undoubtedly efforts to control these agencies are on the increase— F.A.O. aiding administrations wherever possible to improve the protection of crops and harvested materials, and the new Phytosanitary service in Africa aiming at organizing the control of particularly dangerous organisms. But it will be long before an effective control can be exercised in the far-flung fastnesses of the forests and the distant wooded savannas.

Other Aspects of Patterning

In following other lines of thought as to patterning, it is instructive to note these points:

(i) There may be a *family* basis to cultivation, or there may be the basis of an *association* of families within a tribal group—such as a 'kraal' (Spanish *corral*)—in some parts of Africa. The heavier work of clearing for cultivation falls to the men, the routine of cultivation, weeding, reaping and so forth, to the women and children. Herding of livestock is the task either of young boys and youths* or of

* In some countries schooling is calling away children and youths increasingly and thus presents a serious sociological-economic problem.

the women and the old men. The significance of a family basis is important in subsistence and even in some forms of commodity production—for example of cocoa, coffee, coconut, cotton, oil-palm (in Africa but rarely elsewhere) and rubber. Its advantage is that many hands co-operate in carrying out a variety of tasks and at probably the least possible cost.

(ii) The prices paid the cultivator for tropical products normally are lower in proportion than are given in Europe and North America. Exceptions to this, of course, come to mind, such as coffee, tea, cocoa, sisal, cotton, rubber, coconut, palm oil and maize during and since the last war. Subsistence crops—millets, sorghum, cassava, sweet potato, taro, yams, fruits, vegetables and even maize in the more favourable seasons and earlier in the season—often are sold for very little locally. Notable exceptions occur, of course, as in some of the urban areas in Latin America, Ghana, Nigeria and Malaya where crops are sold at comparatively high figures because of transport costs and of the higher income of the purchasers in the towns.

(iii) Rarely do food price controls exist worthy of the name and, if these be promulgated, their practical application is seldom effective. Extremely low prices for a wide range of crops may be paid therefore by the middleman, who often holds some of the items for retail, in the lean months, to the very communities who sold him these originally—but now at iniquitous prices.

(iv) While co-operatives of various kinds may have existed since the turn of the century—for example since 1904 in India—usually only a comparatively small proportion of the cultivators belongs to these. Frequently the co-operatives have been 'run' from above and not from within by the members and their representatives. Furthermore, financial and administrative support is given so freely that the movement has not learned to stand on its own feet but continues to depend upon official help. Even with State funds behind it, the movement frequently still fails to provide sound credit and other facilities for the simple cultivator.

The Popular Call for Mechanization

A favourite request by both the administrations and sectors of the farming communities in underdeveloped countries is for an immediate introduction of and a rapid growth in mechanization. Much ill-founded optimism exists regarding the benefits to be gained by the mechanizing of as many operations in the tropics and hotter subtropics as are found possible in more highly developed countries, under conditions of climate, soil, social setting and economics wholly diverse. This appeal for mechanization is to be heard in a number of African territories and also in some countries in South-East Asia and Latin America. The degree of mechanization pressed for locally quite rightly may be slight—as for the first ploughing of land so as to save time in the early preparation of a seed bed after rain has fallen. Conversely, the requests may be unduly elaborate—as in countries where not only are the vegetation removal, rooting and first preparation of the terrain and the soil demanded, but also the mechanizing of all the operations from sowing to harvesting and processing. Fortunately requests of the last kind have not been taken seriously ... because this would be at the expense of and to the disappointment of the over-eager administrations concerned.

Diversification

As mentioned in Chapter II, the diversification of production in the tropics and the hotter subtropics, either for subsistence or for local sale and export, frequently is wanting or poor. Examples of this appear in Table III. There are, of course, striking exceptions to an approach to a monoculture export economy, for example those countries toward the end of Table III—Ceylon, Malaya-Singapore, Thailand and Indonesia—where significant returns derive from several crops.

Heavy Staffing at Headquarters

In the underdeveloped territories under foreign administration rarely if ever has an excessive personnel existed at headquarters responsible for crop production policy and practice. Indeed it could have been said that more commonly there was insufficient staff for this purpose, with consequent delay in the making and putting into effect of decisions. Today, however, some of the 'new' administrations tend to pile staff upon staff at headquarters, few if any of these knowing anything significant about the economic and the technical details of crop production. This new kind of bureaucrat rarely possesses the administrative qualities of his predecessors of Colonial days but frequently irritates the field staff and, where there is any liaison, the representatives of the farming communities as well. It is hoped that this apparently ever-tightening grip of the bureaucrat will not be permitted to set into a general and fixed pattern but rather is a temporary phase only. It has been said of at least one relevant

International organization as of the Indian Second Development Plan—that the bureaucrats have not added an iota to the production of crops, but talk grandiloquently about so doing!

Problems

Great Challenges

It is unnecessary to discuss the *problems* arising from even these few examples of the *patterns* that exist in crop production in the tropics and subtropics, but all of these present many points demanding study. In review it is worth noting that the features presenting the greatest challenge over all are:

(1) The raising of the efficiency of production of both subsistence and commodity crops, where small cultivators are the principal producers; (2) working out a satisfactory and timely substitute for 'shifting cultivation'; (3) assuring that 'sedentary' farming does not deplete the quality of the soil so rapidly and so extensively that widespread social and economic distress follow; (4) evolving effective ways and means for the technical and economic diversification of cropping; and (5) introducing that growing measure of mechanization best suited to the needs of the local community.

Other Problems

Among other problems, not arising directly from what has been discussed under *Patterns*, the following are the more significant:

Lack of Local Ecological Knowledge

There is an almost all-pervading dearth of knowledge of even the more general, let alone the more detailed, local ecology of the important crop plants. This applies notably to cocoa, coffee, tea, oil-palm, coconut, banana, pepper (*Piper*), sugarcane, rice, soya cotton, sisal, rubber and tobacco. In addition to banana there are also sundry tropical fruits—mango, mangosteen (*Garcinia*), litchi (*Nephelium*), guava (*Psidium*), anonaceous fruits, *Citrus* (orange, grapefruit and mandarin) and pawpaw (*Carica*) that would repay careful investigation, bearing in mind their potential later much increased supply to the temperate markets. This poverty in applied ecological knowledge retards the obtaining of higher, more consistent and better quality yields. But the details of *local* ecology—the interrelation of the plant with the environmental both aerial and edaphic—demand study and interpretation in relation to efficient production.

82

No Appreciation of Timing and Timelyness

In the practice of crop husbandry according to the local bioclimatic setting, relevant detail almost invariably is lacking as to the
timing and timelyness of various operations such as clearing or
thinning of the local vegetation, soil preparation, seeding or planting
cultivation, the balance, programme and timing of fertilizing of the
soil and the organization of harvesting. What has become almost
an up-to-the-hour routine in progressive farming in Europe and
North America for the production of standard crops is not approached
in the tropics—except in the growing of pineapple in Hawaii and
banana in the finest plantations in the most efficient Latin American
'Banana Republics'. So much less is known of local climatic factors
and complexes; the nutrient, physical and biological features of the
soils and their interplay; the responses of the crops to precise kinds
of management and the ecology of the relationships of the *indigenous*
vegetation and the *exotic* crop in regard to pests, diseases, vermin
and ecological competition. Details applying in the humid tropics
may not hold or may vary greatly in the subhumid and the subarid.

Poor Knowledge of Technique of Forest Thinning for Production of Certain Crops

We are still ignorant about the technique and economy of the
thinning or the complete removal of woody growth, for the purpose
of utilizing the ground for the growing of annual and perennial
crops. This is true for cocoa, coffee, pepper, banana and sundry
food crops which may be grown in suitable association with indigenous trees and shrubs left *in situ*, and for those like oil-palm, tea,
rubber, cotton, sisal and plantation banana and annuals suitable for
mechanized cultivation requiring almost complete removal of the
woody growth above and below ground.

The history of each and every larger-scaled enterprise, attempted
on land where removal or thinning of woody growth has been a preliminary requirement, reveals how serious a problem is the effective
clearing or thinning or such growth—compatible with satisfactory
protection of the soil and the economy of investment. Instructive
examples of what not to do are seen in the experiences gained in the
wooded savanna of Tanganyika (East African Groundnuts Scheme),
the jungle of the Dry Zone of Ceylon (Gal Oya Irrigation Scheme) and
in the humid *selva* of Peru (*vide* the valiant efforts of a well-known and
philanthropic American, Mr. R. Letourneau (Phillips, 1959B: 59) to

clear land for pasturage). To these spectacular examples could be added many a small project by both governments and private enterprise from Latin America, through Africa to India and South-East Asia.

Difficulties of Weed Control

Although annual and perennial vegetation, both indigenous and exotic—that is weeds or 'plants out of place' and other growth of no economic value—are known to influence beneficially the rehabilitation of the soil, the control of this highly vigorous vegetation is a most arduous and expensive undertaking. This task faces the simple cultivator in the luxuriant highly humid and the humid forests, in the rice fields where grass, sedge and other unwanted vegetation is lush and in the wooded savanna where, although less luxuriant than in the more humid regions, the growth still is vigorous. Weed control is of course of the greatest importance also to the progressive estate manager and farmer depending to some degree at least upon mechanized equipment.

Apart from incidental information of local interest—as in the use of arsenicals for weed control in the rubber plantations of Malaya —little yet is known of the practical and economic possibilities of extensive control of weeds by chemicals. Selective herbicides and arboricides so far have had a limited and local economic success only, and it will be long before these could be of unfailing practical value to the small cultivator.

Some students of tropical crop production argue that one of the reasons for the relatively small dimensions of so high a proportion of so-called 'farms', in the humid tropics, is the battle the cultivator anticipates he will have to wage against luxuriant weeds. While this perhaps is too sweeping a generalization, I believe that sometimes this is of some importance in regulating the sizes of patches cropped at one and the same time.

Low Proportion of Tropical Soils suitable for Cultivation

The *known* proportions of tropical areas suitable for arable land are relatively low, but in many parts of South America, Africa and South-East Asia no land-use survey worthy of the name ever has been attempted, hence there still is no reliable means of making an assessment. A problem for solution, therefore, is the quickest and least costly but yet sufficiently reliable method and procedure for making this assessment. Aerial photography supported by appropriate ground land-use survey teams studying the main features of the terrain, vegetation, soils and the local farming economy produces most useful information in wooded savanna and subdesert. For dense forest, however, this technique is of little if any service—according to the detailed study by my colleague Dr. R. F. Loxton (1959), my own personal experience and other cognate information.

With so high a proportion of the used arable land in many countries and of the cultivator communities thereon devoted to subsistence cropping, it will be a major difficulty to convert a gradually increasing sector thereof to the discipline of more intensive farming.* Attempts to introduce more intensive methods are certain to follow the provision of irrigation and, of course, the developing of a land hunger in regions of high rainfall: the forests.

This has proved a problem recently on the expanded irrigation projects in India. From my own observations and from the literature I believe this would prove to be true also in many indigenous and naturalized communities in Latin America, Africa and Asia.

Poor Knowledge of Economics of Production

All too little is known of the economy of production both in subsistence and progressive farming. Admittedly the obtaining of meaningful information about the economic significance of the time of a family group spent upon the various operations essential to winning even a limited, simple cereal or other crop, is no easy matter. This is true even when the co-operation and confidence of the family, frequently suspicious of such interest on the part of the outsider, is ensured. Where production is along estate lines and is progressive, it is easier to obtain a working impression of the details of *in-put* and *out-take*. But here again records often are faulty, patchy and ill-designed or in some other way inadequate for the purpose of gaining true information about costings. Direct overhead, maintenance, depreciation and other detailed costs rarely are recorded.

Notable exceptions to this doleful tale occur in some private undertakings in Latin America, the West Indies, the former Belgian Congo, British West Africa, India, Ceylon and Malaya.

Difficulties in Large-scale Co-operative Schemes

Where is it possible to find the appropriate interplay of ecological and economic setting, production potential, sociological conditions

* I am well impressed with the responses of African 'master farmers' in Southern Rhodesia and Nyasaland to extension and general guidance provided by the local Departments of Agriculture. This augurs well for the future development of subsistence and cash crop production in these countries: April, 1961.

and so forth to warrant the attempting of larger-scaled co-operative farming propositions? In light of the continued impression in the minds of many that the 'TVA' and the Gezira approaches (Gaitskell, 1959; Phillips, 1959B) are applicable, *mutatis mutandis*, to any set of circumstances in the underdeveloped world, it is as well to dispel this view now that the special features of both of these splendid undertakings are known to be unlikely to occur in identical or closely similar form elsewhere. India is likely to face this issue in her great expansion of irrigation. She will experience the economic and sociological differences between these and the two classic undertakings mentioned.

The mighty task of developing for crop production some of the vast forest regions (highly humid forest: HHF, and humid forest: HF) and in some countries extensive swamp forest along the great rivers—in Southern America, in the former Belgian Congo and in other parts of tropical Africa and in parts of South-East Asia—will face a number of governments. In these days of internationalism in development, the international organizations such as the World Bank and its related subsidiaries, (I.F.C. and IDA.), F.A.O., W.H.O., W.M.O., I.L.O. and U.N.E.S.C.O. definitely will take their part in furthering the planned development of these immense tracts of heavily wooded country. Herein exist many political, economic, health, educational, transport and technical and managerial agricultural problems. One of the most refractory certainly will be the political-psychological-health-adaptability meshwork of problems associated with propaganda to encourage communities to move from one bioclimatic region to another of very different kind. An example is seen in the thought of moving Indians from the over-populated cool to cold *sierra* of Peru to the almost uninhabited warm and humid *selva* of the Amazon. Similar if less challenging propositions embracing the movement of people could face the authorities and the people in the former Belgian Congo, India, Ceylon, Malaya and elsewhere. Colonization projects of this kind obviously present enormous problems far beyond those of the production of crops and livestock.

Promise

Promise for Development of Crop Production reasonably Fair to Good

On studying the background constituted by the *patterns* and the *problems* of crop production in the humid (HHF and HF) and the more arid regions (SHWS, MSAWS, SAWS) it is clear that, despite many difficulties, a valid argument exists for believing that there is a reasonably good *promise* for *both* subsistence and commodity crops. This applies not only to the already cultivated areas in the more favoured localities but also to those appropriate ones still to be developed. Success, however, depends upon satisfactory policies being formulated, put into effect and consistently maintained in practice. But it is emphasized that this *promise* cannot be fulfilled at a high tempo, at least several decades and more being necessary for the satisfactory development of production, distribution and marketing and their requisite integration.

There is truth in Gourou's (1956) belief that intensive production of food must and will replace the present extensive methods. But my qualification is that this would be feasible in certain ecological settings only, despite Gourou's already mentioned claim that the 'possibility' is rather in man than in the environment. Whether the 'brilliant future' in mind by Gourou for tropical agriculture is in store for more than very limited sectors of the vast tropical-subtropical expanses, however, is debatable. Moreover, man himself yet must prove the fullness of the possibilities latent within him.

(i) *In the Forests*

A high potentiality exists for production in the highly humid (HHF) and the humid (HF) forest regions, because of the interplay of consistent high humidity, high and well distributed rainfall, steady warmth and soils that—while delicate and readily despoiled—are fairly rapidly rehabilitated by the normal processes of biotic succession. Given the requisite care and understanding in their cultivation and conservation these soils, under the biotic circumstances in the forest regions, could produce far greater yields of specific commodity and food crops than at present. Mind, muscle, machine and method and morale must be interwoven in the managing of these soils, so as to yield the best possible results. Although the application of mechanization to cultivation in the forest regions probably never can be great, there are mechanized techniques that could benefit production. These include: (1) Portable mechanical saws for the ready felling of medium to small trees, thus saving heavy manual labour; (2) small tractors with attachments for the discing and other very light preparation of soil on more extensive open areas in 'broken' forest or *induced* savanna, and for light soil and water conservation works; (3) the aerial irrigation of cocoa, coffee, tea,

banana and other perennials liable to suffer from temporary drought;*
(4) sprayers and dusters for insecticides, fungicides and, maybe later,
selective weedicides; (5) smaller-scaled cooling and drying chambers
for the holding of relatively perishable products prior to transporting; and (6) simple processing plants for cereals, plantains and other
food products. These kinds of equipment still demand study regarding the kind of work they must perform and their most appropriate
design compatible with cost.

(ii) In the Wooded Savannas

In the wooded savanna regions where the amount and distribution
of rain is satisfactory (as in the subhumid (SHWS) and subarid
(SAWS) variants) and in the arid (AWS), the subdesert (SD) and
the desert (D) variants where suitable soils could be irrigated, there
also is *promise* of an expansion of acreage and of much higher yields
of food crops and of cotton sisal, hibiscus and other fibres. The
limiting factors in any locality might include accessibility—which
the development of transportation might overcome in due time;
an insufficiency of terrain with suitable topography and soils; and a
scarcity of water for primary and other needs, which modern methods
of water development might alter, provided the locality has been
chosen with this prospect in mind. With a rapidly growing interest
in the understanding of the psychological-political-economic background to farming by the indigenous peoples, it is necessary for the
administration to determine beforehand the reaction of the local
communities to settlement in the areas proposed for development.

Not forgetting the many difficulties facing soil and water conservation, the maintenance of fertility and of soil structure in many parts
of the wooded savanna and the subdesert regions in the three continents and prospective and actual irrigation, it is nevertheless clear
that sound crop and soil husbandry and management of production
could draw much higher yields from subsistence and export crops.
But this presupposes for each country much more intensive and
widely spread research, a more practically experienced, better trained
and a considerably larger agricultural extension service, an effective
practice in community development, and the inspiring of leaders and
of rank and file among the cultivators to learn from practical

* There is great scope for well designed and planned aerial irrigation in
the tropics and subtropics. More intensive investigation, however, is
essential if the best possible results are to be obtained.

demonstration. Furthermore they must heed advice based on local knowledge. Where funds are meagre and personnel sparse in wooded savanna and subdesert regions containing fair to good quality soils, it will be many years before these presuppositions will be more than theoretical.

Psychological Approach to Farmers: Promise Fair

Although the soil and water conservation problems on arable land in the forest and the wooded savanna regions are complex and seem to be appreciated by the local cultivators in limited degree only, there are signs that the psychological-biological-sociological approach is beginning to *promise* fairly well for the future. Where considered and consistently supported endeavours have been made to win the hearts and the minds of the local cultivators and 'mixed' farmers—in the replanning of residential, cropping and livestock areas in localities where a lack of attention to these matters has exacerbated the deterioration of soil, of crops and of natural pasturage and browse—some success is being achieved. Impressive examples of this attempted blending of education, persuasion, demonstration and technical engineering and agricultural practice exist in their preliminary phases in certain African areas in Basutoland, Swaziland and Kenya.* These devoted endeavours of the local British administrations deserve all possible suppor t and should be nurtured with care.

Mechanization of some Promise within Certain Limits

The mechanization of crop-producing practices promises well—from land clearing and preliminary preparation to harvesting, drying and processing in the wooded savanna (subhumid (SHWS)) and in those sectors of the subarid (SAWS) with more reliable rainfall. It also is potentially important where irrigation is provided: in the arid (AWS) and subdesert (SD) regions. Naturally the kind and the degree of mechanization depend entirely upon the climate, the soil types, the range of crops producible on rain-fed land and under irrigation, the standards and the background of the cultivators, and the quality and the coverage of the guidance available. A heavy responsibility rests upon the administrations, the officials, the advisers

* Encouraging progress also is being made in the African areas of Southern Rhodesia and in sectors of Nyasaland.

and all others involved not to press mechanization beyond the conservative limits of safety, otherwise disappointment and serious loss of money and of confidence in both mechanization and those who advocate it inevitably will follow.

Supplementary Irrigation in Forests: Worthy of Study

It is certain that some pattern of supplementary irrigation would be valuable in the forest regions—in the humid (HF), the humid-subhumid (HSF), the montane (HMF) and the less humid montane (HSMF)—for specific crops during the months when the rainfall definitely is less than in periods of equivalent length during the remainder of the year. At first thought, apparently quite illogical, the irrigating of perennial crops such as cocoa, coffee, banana—when their vigour and growth alike are retarded by temporary drought—is seen to be potentially useful when considered objectively. The good responses of banana to overhead irrigation, during a season markedly less moist than the remainder of the year, have been recorded on the plantations of Messrs. Elder and Fyffe in the Southern Cameroons. So good is the promise of this kind of planned addition of moisture in this instance that an endeavour is being made to study the responses of cocoa to a similar kind of treatment on the Kade Research Station, Faculty of Agriculture, Ghana, in humid forest (HF) of 65–80 inches average rainfall but with drier but *not* entirely dry conditions during the months December to March.

There is considerable *promise* in all the continents for the irrigating of suitable soils in satisfactory physiographic setting in the variants of the wooded savanna (SHWS to AWS) and in the sub-desert and the desert (SD, D). While not belittling the magnitude of the challenge of the selection of really satisfactory sites for dams for irrigation, I must stress the equally challenging task of choosing for watering those classes of soils likely to respond satisfactorily to irrigation practices. Failure to select these wisely will result in erosion, leaching and the insidious development of brack or so-called 'black alkali'. Provided this task is accomplished successfully there should be an appreciable expansion in irrigable land in the course of the next fifty years. At the risk of repetition it is worth stressing that within the foreseeable future the conversion of salt and saline water—sea and other—to fresh and the pumping of this over great distances for irrigation will be a possibility. Perhaps, in due time, this may be economic in some regions. This would open new vistas for the developing of coastal subdeserts and deserts as for example in Peru and Chile, Angola, South-West Africa and the Somali Republic and of arid coastal areas in West Pakistan and India.

Richness of Tropical Soils exaggerated, but Soils of Fair Promise

Doubtless the richness of the soils of the tropics, both humid and arid, has been much exaggerated in the minds of administrators, commercial enterprises anxious to 'float' new local projects in agriculture, journalists and even some geographers. But this is no reason for taking the pessimistic view, recently supported by some non-agriculturally experienced scientific writers, that fertility and structure in tropical soils are so definitely *evanescent* that only disaster could follow their development and more intensive use (*vide* Gourou, 1947, 1953; Stamp, 1953).

The truth appears to be that *careful* management is absolutely essential for the maintenance of the fertility and the physico-biotic characteristics of these soils. Provided such a quality of management is assured, the soils should produce *higher* yields, locality for locality, than they now commonly do. Naturally much depends upon the history of the development of these soils—whether in the forests (highly humid (HHF), humid (HF), montane (HMF) and humid-subhumid (HSF))—or in the wooded savanna (subhumid (SHWS) to arid (AWS)), the subdesert and the desert (SD, D).

Again, much depends upon whether the soils are wholly rain-fed or partially or entirely irrigated. As irrigation proceeds, the bogies of leaching, erosion, surface washing and the development of brack appear when the technique of the application of water is unsuitable —the degree of danger depending upon the climatic and soil features in each particular locality. But research, experimentation, pilot trials and other studies should yield information about the management of the soils, the usage of water and the husbandry and protection of the crops—and this should be used to prevent or reduce the evil effects of the process of deterioration.

Undoubtedly in the forest regions the challenge to the agriculturist, the soil scientist and the farmer lies in the discovering of the most practicable and the cheapest ways and means for the farming of land by *sedentary* communities no longer free to indulge in 'shifting cultivation'. With the steady accumulation of experience in all the continents involved there can be no question that this challenge will be met during the next fifty years—always remembering, however, that in the last analysis it is the simple cultivator himself who must be the final arbiter. An ultra-conservative class might prefer to starve rather than adopt a radically new form of cultivation.

Certain Conditions Essential to Fulfilment of Promises

As all hitherto said—under *patterns* and *problems*—is concerned vitally in any *promise* for the future of crop production, it is germane to summarize that the following must be borne in mind or provided if the general fair *promise* of this form of production in the tropics, humid and other, and in the hotter subtropics is to be fulfilled on a scale at all significant:

(1) In South America—at all events in the larger countries—Africa and, to some extent, in parts of South-East Asia not yet heavily populated, there still is scope for an appreciable expansion of arable land.

(2) On land presently arable, including that temporarily resting in a pattern of 'shifting cultivation', immense opportunity still exists for the better maintenance of fertility and structure in the soils and for the improvement of these and of the biotic characteristics.

(3) Agronomic practice on the land of simple cultivators within the forest regions and on those less humid and less moist offers much opportunity for improvement. Better crop husbandry combined with efforts to maintain and ameliorate the quality of the soil would ensure higher yields per unit area and of better grade.

(4) Much good could come from a consistent usage of better seed, of improved strain or variety in relation to yield and capacity for greater resistance to pests and disease. Balanced fertilizers—in the absence of natural manure and compost or in combination therewith—would permit of a more intensive farming of soils on the basis of a *sedentary* as contrasted with a 'shifting' occupation. An effective and consistent protection against diseases, pests, vermin and larger animals destructive to crops in itself could cause great changes in the quality and the quantity of the harvests.

(5) A solution of the problems of tenure well might stimulate cultivators to heed the lessons available through demonstrations and advice—but no rapid response should be expected unless all the forces of suasion, visual demonstration and leadership are co-ordinated. Indeed it is certain that in most underdeveloped countrie these forces must be strengthened greatly if they are to reflect any serious impact within ten to twenty years. Individual ownership—

with appropriate associated conditions—might prove the most satisfactory solution, but this presupposes an agricultural evolution, perhaps a *revolution*, which the various administrations might fear to generate.

(6) The co-operative movement possesses the germ of much that is good, but it must be disciplined, guided, ably led by its own leaders and, within restricted limits, must be given some initial support by the authorities. When the requisite balance of external support and internal initiative and motive force has been struck, this movement could do much to organize the appropriate purchasing of agricultural requirements, the collection, storage and marketing of approved products and the provision of credit for the development of productivity. As the movement and as cultivation practices improve, there should emerge a gradually increasing number of more efficient cultivators or small farmers, capable of leading their fellows toward being better husbandrymen. This *promise* is not yet impressive, except very locally, but the time has been short for the birth of leadership essential to the helping along of the evolution of this more efficient class of cultivator and farmer.

(7) Communications—especially secondary and 'feeder' roads—are known to stimulate the local growing of both subsistence and commodity crops. This is seen clearly in Latin America and West Africa in the expansion of both cocoa and coffee, and in India, Ceylon and South-East Asia in the growing of further acreages of tea and rubber. In West and East Africa the making of 'feeder roads' inevitably stimulates the further growing of the staples—maize, rice, millets, taro, yams, pulses and others according to the bioclimatic conditions.

Carefully planned systems of these classes of road, their establishment at reasonable cost depending upon the terrain, rainfall régime and soil types, together with satisfactory arrangements for their maintenance, would go far toward stimulating production in the more favourable localities like the humid forest (HF), the montane forest (HMF, HSMF) and the better portions of the subhumid savanna (SHWS), hitherto isolated from the districts needing more food and other agricultural materials.

(8) Wherever feasible, the production of subsistence and export crops should be closely interlinked. Depending naturally upon the suitability of the region and the distance from and the communications with the markets, this approach to an integrated agricultural

development should prove more viable economically than the growing of subsistence crops only.

(9) Admittedly not everywhere feasible, but depending upon the local bioclimatic conditions, the traditions of the local people and kindred factors, the greater expansion of 'mixed' farming—that is the combining of livestock with arable farming—should prove advantageous both to the soil and to the community's socio-economic welfare. This is a psychological, sociological and ecological challenge, demanding infinite tact, care and ability in those who would attempt to solve it gradually.

(10) Social welfare and community development in the humid forest as well as in the wooded savanna regions should help to make the cultivators happier, especially the younger members of the community. This should help to restrain the tendency for the younger men to seek the supposed pleasures of the 'bright lights' of the urban districts, where so often disillusionment and poverty await them. The establishment of local shopping centres, wherein consumer goods are readily available, also would stimulate the local cultivators to work and thus to gain a little more for their women and themselves: something just beyond the immediate domestic needs.

In Ghana some very useful social welfare and community development work in rural areas has been described by du Sautoy (1958). Similar approaches elsewhere might bring forth equally encouraging responses on the part of the rural communities.

CHAPTER V

Pasturage, Animal Production and Health

For the sake of ease of discussion the main points and issues are considered under these heads:

   (I) *The Ecology and Management of Pasturage and Browse.*
  (II) *Animal Husbandry and Production.*
 (III) *Animal Health.*

(I) The Ecology and Management of Pasturage and Browse

Definition

For all practical purposes *pasturage* in the sense implied here covers all natural vegetation in which grasses predominate as food for livestock, but in which there usually are some sedges, herbaceous and sometimes a small proportion of subshrub growth.

The grasses commonly occur in communities that are *not* climax. That is they occur in either *proclimax* or *subclimax* stages leading to a climax in which grasses often play little if any part. Pasturage therefore may range from secondary prostrate and short grasses (to 12 inches) to very tall ones such as *Pennisetum purpureum* ('Elephant Grass', over 12 feet high) in Africa and *Imperata cylindrica* ('Lalang' of almost the same height) in Asia and Africa.

In the forest and the wooded savanna regions (subhumid to arid: SHWS to AWS) the grasses are not climax and may be frequent to occasional to rare according to the nature of the canopy and the density of the woody growth, the stage of the plant succession and the manner in which the vegetation has been treated by the cultivator, the pastoralist and the 'mixed' farmer. In growth-form the pasturage may be constituted by carpet or sod-forming grasses—as in the humid regions—or by small or large bunch (tussock) grasses—as in the wooded savannas and the less severe variants of the subdesert. Their *basal area*, that is the permanent coverage of the soil for which they are responsible, may range from about 50 to 90 per cent for the carpet grasses to less than 1 to 5 per cent for the bunch and open-type stoloniferous forms, especially in the arid and subdesert regions. The stems and leaves of the grasses may be lax and soft to luscious, as in the humid regions, or hard wiry, narrow and inrolled, as in some of the wooded savanna regions (subarid to arid: SAWS to AWS). In the subdesert regions (AWS/SD, SD, SD/D) they usually are hard-stemmed, narrow and inrolled-leaved, wiry bunch grasses of very low basal area: from 3 to less than 1 per cent. Their palatability and their nutrient values may be high to mediocre to very poor. Some species are markedly palatable to wild herbivores and livestock in some seasons but much less so in others, while others are unpalatable at all stages and times.

Climax pasturages do exist, of course, in the tropics and the hotter subtropics, but are far less extensive than their *proclimax* and *subclimax* counterparts. They are restricted to certain less severe subdesert/desert transition zones or *ecotones* (SD/D), to high country in the subtropics where frost and cold are severe in the dry season (3000 to 7000 feet) and to montane and high montane regions—from 9000 to 14,000 feet and upwards. *Pasturage* in all the regions other than the highly humid (HHF) and humid (HF) is subjected to annual or erratic burning commonly caused by man. Indeed, fire plays an important rôle in the ecology and management of all such communities. Some of the tropical and a rather higher proportion of the subtropical grasses are particularly suited to systematic grazing and burning, and may be mown to advantage. Their response to mowing and fertilizing usually is excellent. Some of the more leafy species make good ensilage when cut at the right stage. Depending upon the region, they may be highly nutritious (protein and minerals) or may serve largely as roughage. The humid regions (HHF and HF) and the subhumid (SHWS) generally produce the less nutritious but the more luscious pasturage, the more arid (subarid to subdesert: SAWS, AWS, AWS/SD and SD) the much less lush but the more nutritious.

Where pasturage is *proclimax* and *subclimax*—that is the existing grassland is due to some factor or agency controlling the successional development at several stages or one stage below the *climax*—a withholding of fire and a low grazing pressure will accelerate the development of the community toward a *climax* woody growth, scrub, thicket, tall bush or even forest.

Browse—in the sense here implied—embraces all edible growth:

from short semi-woody subshrubs of a foot or less in height to large woody shrubs and trees up to about 20 to 30 feet high. Foliage, twigs, branchlets, flowers, fruits, seed and bark—some or all—may be browsed by cattle, goats and even hardy sheep. More highly developed in the subhumid to subdesert regions (SHWS to SD), browse also is a feature in the highly humid, the humid and the humid-subhumid regions (HHF, HF, HSF), where a fair proportion of shrubs and trees provide tasty morsels for wild and domesticated browsing animals. Browse plants are mingled with pasturage—especially in the wooded savannas—but may occur almost pure, as in the notable subdesert Karoo (SD–ST) in Southern Africa and in mixed evergreen and deciduous thickets up to 30 to 40 feet tall in tropical wooded savanna (SHWS to SAWS to AWS) in South America, Africa and the less humid portions of Asia. The mismanagement of mixed pasturage and browse leads to the reduction of pasturage in favour of the shrub and tree vegetation, as discussed later.

Ecological Setting

A summary of the ecological status, comparative suitability of the local pasturage and browse for extensive usage and the possibilities of establishment of pasturage in the major bioclimatic regions in Latin America, Africa and Asia appears in Table V.

Man's rôle is profound in changing the details of the ecological setting, either through amelioration of the environment and its related biotic communities or, much more frequently, through spoliation thereof. His influences through the over-stocking of natural pasturage and browse; his provision of water where none previously existed or his augmenting of weak or seasonal supplies; his mowing and fertilizing of native grazing; his growing of green and other fodder and his preparation of ensilage—these activities and others are acting either for evil or for good in more and ever more localities in the *bioclimatic* regions noted in Table V. Thus the original *biotic* equilibrium—delicate, very lightly poised and therefore readily disturbed as it is so often—has been converted to what the modern American sociological economists like to term '*disequilibrium*', noted more fully in Chapter VII.

After many years of study of the literature and of investigation in Africa, supported by observations in other parts of the tropics, I am impressed with the seriousness of the *growing threat* to the well-being

TABLE V

REGIONAL FEATURES OF PASTURAGE AND BROWSE*

Region	Status†	Comparative Suitability‡	Possibilities for established pasturage§
HHF: highly humid forest	P	Med–Sl (B)	Mod–Med, (locally H)
HF: humid forest	P	Mod–Med (B)	Mod–Med, (locally VH–H)
HSF: humid-subhumid forest	P and S	Mod–Med (B)	Med–Sl
HMF: humid montane forest	P	Mod–Med locally H (B)	Mod (locally H–VH)
HSMF: humid-subhumid montane forest	P and S	Mod–Med	Mod–Med
PF: periodically flooded forest	P and S	Med–Sl in wet seasons, but may be Mod in dry (B)	Mod–Med, (locally H)
RF: riverine and flood plain forest	P and S	Med in wet season, but Mod in dry	Mod–Med, (locally H)
SHWS: subhumid wooded savanna	P, S and C	H–Mod (BF)	Mod–Med
SAWS: subarid wooded savanna	P, S and C	H–Mod–Med (BF)	Med–Sl, unless irrigated
AWS: arid wooded savanna	P, S and C	H–Mod–Med, cattle, sheep and goats (BF)	Sl–Nil, unless irrigated
SD: subdesert	P, S and C	Mod–Med–Sl, locally H; (B), in some types (BF) sheep, goats, locally camel	Nil, unless irrigated
D: desert, less severe, oases	P, S and C	Mod–Med, to Sl around oases seasonally; (B) sheep, goats, camel	Nil, unless irrigated

98

TABLE V—*continued*

Region	Status†	Comparative Suitability‡	Possibilities for established pasturage§
OG: open grassland:			
subtropical upland	P, S and C	(H)–Mod–Med	Sl to locally Mod–H
montane	Usually C	do.	do.
high montane	Locally S and P	do.	do.
subdesert	C	Mod–Med–Sl, sheep, goats	Nil, unless irrigated

* In column (3): (B) indicates that *browse* is as important as *pasturage*; (BF) indicates *browse* is fairly important.

† P: proclimax ⎫ stage
  S: subclimax ⎬ principally
  C: climax ⎭ grazed or browsed.

‡ VH: very high
  H: high
  Mod: moderate
  Med: mediocre
  Sl: slight
  ( ) occasional, not usual.

§ Sown and planted, usually the better indigenous grasses but locally certain chosen exotics, including legumes, not irrigated unless stated.

of the natural pasturage and browse. More especially do I fear a steady and severe deterioration in the arid, the subarid and the subdesert regions (SAWS, AWS, AWS/SD and SD) and, locally as in South Africa, in the open grassland both proclimax and climax (OGS) and the Karoo subdesert (SD–ST).*

A consideration of the *patterns*, *problems* and *promise* of grazing and browse in the regions under review suggests certain points worthy of note:

(1) It is possible to divide the peoples occupied with livestock husbandry into several general classes: (*a*) The true and often wholly or partially nomadic pastoralists who pay very little if any attention to even the most casual cultivation in favourable localities and

* The situation may be serious, but often is not beyond the wit of man to rectify. *Timely* measures could prevent further wastage.

seasons. (*b*) Those who attempt to win an incidental subsistence crop in the more favourable sites and seasons. (*c*) Those who are or tend to be 'mixed' farmers, with livestock and cultivation associated to mutual advantage.

These classes of pastoralists have their own particular *patterns* of activity and their own *problems* of simple technical and economic nature. In their several ways they exhibit some *promise* of achieving a better living in the future provided they are prepared to submit to some fairly simple self-disciplining and for a modicum of practical advice and guidance. Briefly, the following can be said of these peoples:

(*a*) *Nomadism*, in the sense of patterned movement over long to very long distances according to a cycle of a year or longer, and *transhumance*, or movement to and fro over a much shorter distance seasonally, are still fairly common in parts of the arid to subdesert and subdesert/desert regions of Africa (AWS–AWS/SD–SD–SD/D). Although the nomads are of various types which cannot be elaborated here, it is germane that these are divisible into: (i) Far-ranging groups possessing and dependent largely upon camels or dromedaries. (ii) Groups whose movements, although extensive, traverse country permitting the driving of goats as well as camels. (iii) Groups who traverse long distances, but through country conducive to the driving of sheep as well as goats and camels. (iv) Those whose range is so restricted that cattle, as well as small stock and camels, may be driven reasonable distances from one watering point to another.

There is considerable complexity in the interplay of tradition and the dictates and variations in the arid to sub-desert/desert environment (AWS to SD/D), and these the local groups have learned to live with ecologically—and usually with great success, except in the excessively severe years which occur sporadically.

Due in some measure to political influences, but more largely to technical, psychological and sociological changes in the peoples claiming rights to adjacent terrain formerly almost wholly at the behest of the nomads for purposes of migratory grazing and browse, there has been some interference recently with the earlier almost free movement of the nomadic peoples. This freedom, of course, has been special and relative, in that the patterns of movement according to locality, season and cycle of years have been subject to the nomads' own unwritten but precise and severe codes of behaviour, an infringement of which may result in loss of livestock and even of life itself.

Supported in spirit by the expression of a desire on the part of certain Western administrative authorities, churches and students to 'settle' these migrant peoples, and in practice by the provision through American or other assistance of water for man and beast in places where, for practical purposes, it did not exist before or exist in sufficient amount for a long enough time, this interference is tending to enforce upon, or make attractive to some nomads a life that is either *sedentary* or much more so than they ever hitherto experienced.

The wisdom of the statements of policy expressed and the practicability of the procedure and methods so far employed are open to serious criticism: the heart is running away with the head. To wish to end nomadism conjures up a long train of complex issues of traditional, pastoral, economic and even political nature—issues no one yet has studied sufficiently deeply and for which no easy solutions yet exist. To attempt to 'end' nomadism without providing an adequate alternative way of life likely to fit into the pattern of the climates, soils, vegetation and human sociology involved would be to create far more recondite pastoral and human problems than a termination of nomadism ever could solve. Much like 'shifting cultivation', so vociferously but unintelligently railed against in some well-intentioned international and other circles, *nomadism and transhumance are ecological adaptations to the rigours of a stern environment.*

However beneficial in some respects the provision of water to the migrants might be for a short time and locally, this is a partial solution only. In the absence of appropriately distributed water points, firmly controlled grazing and browsing of the terrain served by these, and a consistent system for the restriction of livestock in numbers according to a watering programme, the last state of the locality and thus of man and beast is certain to be worse than the first. Indications of this introduction of a new tangle of problems, where previously the major issues were much simpler, are to be seen in the Somali Republic and in a small measure in the Bechuanaland Protectorate, indications which correspond with those long since noted in the subdesert Karoo (SD–ST) and the subarid to arid wooded savanna of the Transvaal bushveld (SAWS–ST, AWS–ST). The setting in Northern Nigeria and elsewhere, subarid to arid to subdesert, West Africa (SAWS–AWS–AWS/SD), Equatorial Africa and East Africa also is dangerously appropriate for similar deterioration.

(*b*) Grouped together here, the other classes of pastoralist in varying measure are attempting to arrange some interplay of cultivation with the running of flocks and herds. Where the bioclimatic setting is favourable for livestock but only doubtfully and erratically so for cultivation, the growing tendency to risk an expansion of the latter inevitably will result in disillusionment. It is essential that national and international technical aid and financial assistance be critically applied in these delicate marginal to submarginal regions. Conversely, where the bioclimatic indications are favourable to a sliding scale of cultivation and livestock, sensibly planned investigations and pilot projects should be capable of guiding the local people toward a satisfactory balance.

Because 'mixed' farming has been successful in some European-farmed localities in Latin America and in subtropical and upland tropical Africa (HMF, HSMF, OGS), it is no justification for the general encouragement of indigenous pastoralists to become 'mixed' farmers overnight. We must save these people from the zealots!

(2) A definition of what is implied by pasturage and browse appears earlier in this Chapter, but it is imperative to note here the often remarkable *sensitivity* of some of the grasses and subshrubs to the intensity, season and duration of grazing or browsing. Careless pasturing and browsing soon may reduce the proportion of palatable, nutritious and otherwise valuable species, and thus automatically encourage the early assumption of dominance or increased ecological importance by those kinds either less palatable or wholly unpalatable (*vide* Phillips, 1956; 1959B).

It is ironical that the satisfactory economic management of natural pasturage and browse, throughout the tropics and subtropics, should be one of the *most difficult of agricultural tasks*, demanding general and local experience and ability of a high order. Almost invariably these qualities are not forthcoming in those responsible for the guidance of the local pastoralist.* This is not to forget that not infrequently there is a verbally transmitted local lore of simple management accumulated down the centuries by observant herdsmen and owners, providing information certainly worthy of investigation by means of specially designed observation and field experi-

* The language barrier often is responsible for the lack of understanding between native farmers and expatriate advisers.

mentation. Some attempt to do this is being made at the Research Station, Nungua, Faculty of Agriculture, Ghana, by R. Rose Innes (1959, 1961), who has attempted to study the practices of local pastoralists on the Accra Plains.

Although some herdsmen may understand in their own simple manner the implications of transgressing the unwritten laws of the wild, they usually lack a sense of responsibility to posterity, and therefore engage in practices which they know are detrimental to the ultimate welfare of the natural vegetation. In extenuation of this criticism of the indigenous pastoralist in Latin America and Africa, I must mention that an all too high proportion of farmers of European background and extraction in Central and South America, South, Central and East Africa also fail to show a clear appreciation of what is owed to those still unborn.

(3) The carrying capacity of the natural pasturage and browse in the *forest* regions (HHF and, more particularly, the HF and HMF) sometimes is stated to be relatively high—one/two to three acres per mature cattle unit, equivalent, say, to four to five small stock. From observations in Nicaragua, Peru, Africa, Ceylon and Malaya I should consider these figures too optimistic for continuous grazing and browsing of average pasturage throughout the seasons. In Central and South America, specially suitable exotic grasses, such as some of the African *Panicum* spp., *Hyparrhenia rufa*, *Pennisetum purpureum* and *Digitaria* spp., indeed might provide locally a lush growth capable of carrying a beast to an acre to two acres for a year or more, but it is doubtful whether even this could continue for long. Indigenous pasturage and browse are less likely to show a sustained capacity for this relatively heavy stocking, unless of specially high nutritive quality and exceptional vigour and volume of growth.

In the subhumid wooded savannas (SHWS) the capacity may be of the order of one mature cattle unit to six to ten acres, in the subarid variant (SAWS) from twelve/fifteen to twenty acres, in the arid variant (AWS) twenty to thirty acres, and in the subdesert (SD) forty to one hundred and even more acres. These gross values are based upon the existence of an adequate water supply within some hours' to a day's livestock march and there being *no* supplementary fodder of any kind—hay, stubble, stover, ensilage—available. Obviously the provision of appropriate amounts and kinds of supplementary fodder materially changes the picture. This is significant for the day when irrigation allows the production of supplementary fodder and, perhaps, even that present chimera, 'irrigated pasturage', to develop into something really valuable.

(4) Extensive pasturing and browsing are normally the only practicable form of usage—only on rare occasion is it feasible to produce either high-class natural or established pasturage and to ensure the maintenance of this by intensive management. Were carefully selected localities in the highly humid (HHF) and in the humid forest (HF) and montane forest (HMF) regions to be sown or planted to indigenous or exotic grasses of proven response and quality, and were these pastures to be well maintained in fertility and composition, it might become more fashionable for the more progressive farmers to attempt similar undertakings. Until then the pattern of casual establishment and little or no management of sown or planted pasturage is likely to prevail. Official and private enterprise has shown initiative in parts of Central America and in Peru in attempting to establish exotic pasturage in the humid forest regions: but the standards still are far lower than they should be.

(5) Except in the highly humid and humid forest regions (HHF and HF) fire plays a most important part in the ecology and the simple management of pasturage and browse. Discussed in some detail elsewhere (*vide* Phillips (1930B; 1936; 1959B), and Cook (1939) in Africa and Bartlett (1956) more generally), fire is known to be a *good servant*. This is when it is used with discretion at the right time, in the right circumstances and in relation to the after-grazing and after-browsing of the resultant vigorous regrowth stimulated by the burning. Indeed without fire it would be difficult to 'manage' much of the natural growth on broken ground and steep grades, far from roads, in most parts of the tropics and subtropics. On the other hand, fire is definitely a *bad master* when used indiscriminatively, as it usually is by indigenous and foreign and also by some of the more progressive pastoralists.

Like 'shifting cultivation' and 'nomadism-transhumance' the use of fire has incurred much unwarrantable criticism from some who sincerely wish pastoralists and 'mixed' farmers in the underdeveloped lands all possible progress. Until some practicable alternative has been discovered for ready and widespread application for the control of selectively utilized pasturage and browse, fire must remain the most valuable, the easiest and the cheapest means of control. Where well-regulated usage by livestock, and mowing, are not possible because of the nature of the terrain, the vegetation and the expense, the use of fire is essential to the maintenance of some semblance of order in the unkempt plant communities involved.*

(6) On all the most progressive farms or ranches on relatively unbroken terrain owned and managed by foreigners it is not practicable to mow, graze and otherwise manage intensively the pasturage and browse in the tropics and hotter subtropics. Variable palatability and growth-form render reasonably uniform grazing impossible. Not only do many physical obstacles—woody growth, termitaria great and small, rocks and topography—render impossible the mowing of natural pastures except locally at high cost, but so also does the carrying capacity and therefore the financial return from these. Where controlled grazing and consistent mowing are feasible, a definite improvement in the quality of the wild pastures usually is demonstrable. But this is rarely true of subshrub browse, perhaps because of the inherent difficulty in browsing and mowing effectively this often heterogenous mixture of semiwoody and sometimes subsucculent growth of the most variable botanical composition and palatability. If fire be withheld, the heavier browse occurring in woodland, thicket and scrub obviously cannot be controlled effectively. No satisfactory herbicide or arboricide yet has been discovered, for large-scaled use against heavy, mixed browse of the kind so common in the tropics and hotter subtropics.

(7) Because of its proven significance under suitable circumstances in the temperate regions and its fair promise in certain conditions on progressive farms in the semi-developed subtropics, the fertilizing of pasturage in the tropics and hotter subtropics is advocated by enthusiasts generally wholly inexperienced in the management and economy of pasturage in these underdeveloped regions. Although excellent responses to nitrogen and to nitrogen with phosphorus—but rarely to potash—are demonstrable where the terrain, the amount and the distribution of rainfall, the plant community and the managerial ability of the pastoralist reasonable, the promiscuous application of fertilizers to natural pasturage and short subshrub browse cannot be other than wasteful of time, effort and money.

* In 1932 General Smuts asked me to write the Ten Commandments about burning of veld in South Africa. At first surprised that I should say this was impossible, because a 'Thou Shalt Not' in one region, season or circumstance might be converted to a 'Thou Shalt' in another region, season or circumstance, the General later saw the point and relieved me of my impossible task. I would find it no more possible today!

This 'hot spot' of interest by would-be helpful persons, unaware of the problems involved, should be resisted in the interests of the pastoralist and, in the long run, of the wider use of fertilizers when more is known about their economic application.*

A frequently recurring point is the emphasis laid by some advisers on the necessity for providing *trace* elements in natural pasturage in the tropics and hotter subtropics. Although intensive research doubtless would reveal specific examples of the lack of such elements —as was done by Trumble and others in a sector of Australia—it is likely that a reasonable treatment with nitrogen and phosphorus often would provide the requisite additional fertility.

(8) A major and growing threat is the accelerated encroachment of subshrub and also taller woody growth (up to about 30 feet) into areas previously bearing either a preponderance of grass associated with the tall shrubs and trees, or of palatable browse yielded by subshrubs. Mentioned in Chapter II as a feature reducing the productivity of livestock husbandry and again referred to in Chapter VII as an example of loss of biotic balance or '*disequilibrium*', this insidious be-thicketing or 'bushing-up' of the wooded savannas of the three continents must be mentioned once again as one of the challenges to local administrations and to international organizations alike. (*Vide* Galpin (1926), Phillips; (1934; 1935A and B) for early comments on the ecology of the acceleration of encroachment and Phillips (1959B) for later references.†)

(9) In the subhumid to subdesert regions (SHWS, SAWS, AWS, AWS/SD and SD) the hazards in the development of water are numerous and profound. Water may be unobtainable except at great depth, involving deep boring at heavy cost and the provision and maintenance of expensive mechanized pumping equipment. Occasionally to frequently, according to the climate and the geology, the water is so heavily mineralized as to be useless to man and beast —especially in arid to subdesert/desert regions. In certain geological formations, such as for example the Basement Complex in East Africa, the proportion of blanks and of low-yielding borings may

* The risk of verminosis, due to heavy and consistent stocking of pasturage stimulated by wise fertilizing, also must be anticipated—particularly by sheep farmers.

† As early as July 1925 General Smuts drew my attention to this potential threat to wooded savanna in Africa. He had seen great changes in the Transvaal since 1899, and had observed induced thicketing by *Dichrostachys* and *Acacia* in German East Africa in 1916.

be very high. Surface waters—stored by means of dams—often can be increased in volume and improved in distribution in some countries. In others where the physiography is unsuitable, the shallow depth of the dams entails too heavy an evaporation loss: the gross annual values being as high as 72 inches from open-surface evaporimeters in subhumid wooded savanna near the coast in Ghana, and over 80 to 100 inches in the arid to subdesert wooded savanna in the Bechuanaland Protectorate.

As already mentioned, the provision of water in arid to subdesert regions where it hitherto was either much more sparse or did not exist at all, sets a pattern of scrub encroachment and soil erosion that may become very serious. Consequently this *'disequilibrium'* reacts unhappily upon the people and their livestock attracted to settle around the new watering points. In the absence of control of the local numbers of livestock and the restricting of their drinking at specific points to particular times in accordance with the circumstances prevailing at the time, a haphazard provision of water in localities of this kind does more harm than good.

(10) Rarely possessed either by the native pastoralist or the advisers on pastoral management in the tropics and subtropics, the art of selecting pasturage and browse according to their ecological settings and types demands closer study than it yet has been given. Only recently and very locally has this been attempted by experienced ecologists in parts of South Africa, Southern Rhodesia, Tanganyika and Kenya. Damage follows where too many and too diverse types of vegetation are included in 'camps' for the carrying of livestock—and the details vary with the kind of livestock and the plant communities.

Until more is known of the ecological development of the various major plant or biotic communities in any locality, the 'living fence', the herdsman, is far safer than the immobile wire one. After some years of experience with the informed use of herdsmen for restricting animals to selected grazing and browsing types within a given locality, an acute observer should be able to separate selected portions for management, with some sound reason for the hypothesis that they form compatible ecological pasturage or browse units.

I emphasize a fundamental point that must be made at this stage: the basic ecological successional relations of the vegetation subjected to grazing and browsing must be understood increasingly clearly, if the best results ultimately are to be obtained from any prescribed system of management. Some simple pastoralists inherently appear to understand this and accordingly maintain the vegetation in their own localities, or along their lines of migration, in remarkably good condition. But this is not understood by the majority of pastoralists, if the wretched condition of the vegetation, the soil and the livestock be a criterion. Nor are all advisers blameless.

(11) Since the war a number of authorities have paid some attention to the desirability of resting *arable* land in the tropics and the hotter subtropics, particularly in the subhumid and subarid regions (SHWS, SAWS) and in the *induced* grassland therein. Erroneously this has been accepted by some as being equivalent to what are known as 'leys' in temperate agricultural practice. In point of fact, while the 'leys' usually are sown to grass or other annuals, the resting arable or fallows in the tropics and hotter subtropics are colonized by indigenous grasses, annual and perennial, arising either from seed or from rhizomes. These *secondary* communities usually are efficient in rehabilitating the soil physically and, to some extent, in fertility. Moreover useful grazing thus is available for the livestock owned by the cultivators. This natural development of grass dispenses with the need for attempting to sow or plant it.

In parts of Central and South America the sowing or planting of African grasses—such as *Panicum maximum*, *P. coloratum*, *Cenchrus ciliaris*, *Hyparrhenia rufa*, *Setaria* spp., *Pennisetum purpureum* and *Pennisetum* spp., *Digitaria* spp. and *Cynodon plectostachyum*—on resting arable land in the humid forest region has met with some success, but the economics of this practice still must be examined. In moister, cooler to coldish upland to montane regions in Peru the otherwise useful pasture grass, *Pennisetum clandestinum* ('Kikuyu'), introduced from Kenya, allegedly by Colonel Storey, has taken wide command of arable land since 1922 and now is dubbed 'public enemy Number One' by the local farmers (Phillips, 1959A).

(12) Passing reference was made in (3) above to the 'chimera' of irrigated pastures. Much is spoken by enthusiastic advocates about the remarkable possibilities of establishing pastures under irrigation in the tropics. On a much sounder basis Whyte, Moir and Cooper (1959) have covered the related topic of irrigated pasturage in several subtropical countries and have referred, in passing, to some aspects of irrigation of grasses in the tropics under somewhat special conditions.

Doubtless the successful production of irrigated pastures in the tropics could be accomplished on a fair scale, provided the appropriate grasses were established effectively and were given the care and management essential to their maintenance. As these conditions rarely if ever can be met in one and the same proposition in the tropics, the acreage of really satisfactory pasturage under irrigation is negligible.

Grasses for cutting as green feed for ensilage and possibly for hay—this last in the less humid areas only—readily can be grown under irrigation, but their *management when grazed* is a wholly different matter. Trampling of the pasturage, puddling of the soil and the consequent deterioration of the cover and invasion by weeds are the usual outcome of such ventures on other than carefully directed experimental areas.* Intensive investigation as well as pilot projects should be undertaken and the results therefrom analysed and coordinated before wide-spread pasturage under irrigation are advocated.

(13) It might be asked why nothing hitherto has been said about the selection and breeding of grasses for the tropics, humid and arid. The reason is that while there are irrefutable academic arguments in favour of attempting to do with the tropical and subtropical grasses what has been accomplished so ably for the temperate species in Britain, Europe and North America, the standard of agricultural education of the vast majority of pastoralists and farmers in the tropics and subtropics argues against this at this stage. They would not know how to apply any information which might derive from genetical and selection studies. Furthermore, there are excellent grasses, usually indigenous but also a few introducible, which could be given serious attention in the preparatory period. Basic and applied breeding studies of the kind so successful in temperate species could come later or could be commenced as mainly academic projects in the various bioclimatic regions. For the next twenty-five years, however, there is a sufficiency of material ready to hand for practical use.

(14) In the natural pasturage and browse of the tropics and hotter subtropics legumes certainly occur in many genera and species, herbaceous, subshrub, shrub and tree. Only a small proportion of these, however seems to be taken by livestock. Apart from indigenous

* Exotic *Paspalum dilatatum* and other grasses do well for a time under sewage effluent in the subtropics—good examples being at Johannesburg, South Africa.

clovers at the higher elevations in montane regions in South America and Africa, the browse and the pods of many species of *Acacia* in Africa, and various subshrubs in the three continents, there are few examples of indigenous perennial legumes of outstanding significance in the tropics and subtropics. Annual legumes such as *Vigna* (cow-pea) and *Mucuna* and perennials such as *Cajanus* (pigeon-pea), however, may be cultivated for fodder, or residues thereof are fed to home-based animals. One of the most pressing needs in tropical and subtropical pastoral management is the discovering of relatively efficient and inexpensive methods for the introduction of hardy palatable and non-toxic legumes into natural and established pasturage and natural browse. Although not directly relevant to this particular aspect of the problem, some useful information regarding legumes in the tropics and subtropics has been compiled by Whyte, Nilsson-Leissner and Trumble (1953), while a list of edible legumes in Africa has been prepared by F.A.O./C.C.T.A. (1959).

(II) Animal Husbandry and Production

A general impression of the interrelation of the *bioclimatic* regions and the potentiality for improved production of livestock is gained from Table VI, the main features of which should be compared with those in Table V regarding the suitability of pasturage and browse in the *bioclimatic* regions.

A consideration of Tables V and VI shows that while the tropics and hotter subtropics neither provide really first class conditions of pasture and browse nor *promise* on the average much more than a moderate to mediocre potential for the future development of livestock, nonetheless a fairly good basis exists for expecting that more and better livestock could be produced in the future. It already has been argued that provided certain precautions and actions be taken, the conservation and some measure of improvement of natural pasturage and browse could be achieved in the course of, say, twenty-five years. It also is arguable that selection and breeding of livestock —notably of cattle and goats—could produce *eco-types* that are better adjusted to the rigours of the humid or the arid environments. Some of the still somewhat elementary investigations being conducted in Central and South America—notably in the *selva* of Costa Rica and Peru—could form the basis for the selection of more suitable cattle types for the warm and humid regions (HHF and HF).

Similarly the work by the Bonsma brothers and associates (1948–53) in the Transvaal should assist toward the selection of cattle capable of withstanding better the rigours of the more arid wooded savannas (SAWS, AWS, AWS/SD). Some useful preliminary work is being done on native cattle in Southern Rhodesia.

TABLE VI

REGIONAL POTENTIALITY FOR IMPROVED LIVESTOCK PRODUCTION IN THE TROPICS AND HOTTER SUBTROPICS

Region		Potentiality*	Comment†
HHF:	highly humid forest	Med–Sl	cattle, sheep, goats, pigs, poultry
HF:	humid forest	Mod–Med–Sl	,,
HF-ST:	,, ,, (subtropics)	H–Mod–Med	,,
HSF:	humid-subhumid forest	(H)–Mod–Med	,,
HMF:	humid montane forest	,,	,,
HMF-ST:	,, ,, ,, (subtropics)	H–Mod	,,
HSMF:	humid-subhumid montane forest	H–Mod–Med	,,
PF:	periodically flooded forest	Med–Sl	cattle, sheep, goats
RF:	riverine forest	Med in drier seasons	,,
SHWS:	subhumid wooded savanna	(VH)–H–Mod‡	cattle, sheep, goats, pigs, poultry
SHWS-ST:	,, ,, ,, (subtropics)	(VH)–H–Mod‡	,,
SAWS:	subarid ,, ,,	,,	,,
SAWS-ST:	,, ,, ,,	H–Mod–Med‡	sheep, goats
AWS:	arid ,, ,,	(VH)–H–Mod‡	cattle, sheep, goats
AWS-ST:	,, ,, ,,	(H)–Mod–Med‡	cattle, sheep, goats
SD:	subdesert	Mod‡	sheep, goats, camel
SD-ST:	subdesert (subtropics)	VH–Mod‡	sheep, goats
OG:	open grassland (subtropics) upland	(VH)–H–Mod‡	cattle, sheep, goats, pigs, poultry
	montane	VH–Mod	,,
	subdesert	Med–Sl‡	,,

* VH: very high
H: high
Mod: moderate
Med: mediocre
Sl: slight
( ) occasional, not usual
‡ Presupposes the availability of water within a reasonable distance and a satisfactory measure of control of pests and diseases.

† Refers to local or naturalized livestock.

Assuming that research and practical trials could produce varieties of somewhat higher grades of cattle capable of fair productivity in the highly humid and the humid regions (HHF and HF) and in the subhumid to more arid regions (SHWS to AWS/SD), there would remain the equally difficult matter of leading the small pastoralist— be he an American Indian or a *Mestizo*, an African or an Asian—to husband and keep in good condition and health the animals he owns

TABLE VII

EXPORTS OF MEAT, DAIRY PRODUCTS AND HIDES/SKINS FOR ALL COUNTRIES RECORDED
AS EXPORTING ONE OR ALL OF THESE ITEMS: TROPICS AND SUBTROPICS OTHER THAN
OCEANIA

(in millions of U.S. dollars)*

Country	Year	Meat	Dairy products	Hides/Skins
Costa Rica	1956	0·1	0·1	—
Dominican Republic	1955	0·6	0·1	0·1
	1956	0·3	0·2	—
El Salvador	1955	—	0·2	—
	1956	—	0·3	—
Honduras	1954	—	0·1	0·1
	1955	—	0·2	0·1
Jamaica	1955	—	0·2	0·1
	1956	—	0·2	0·1
Mexico	1954	4·6	1·0	—
	1955	2·6	1·1	—
Nicaragua	1955	—	0·1	—
	1956	—	0·1	—
Panama	1955	—	—	0·1
	1956	—	—	0·1
Trinidad–Tobago	1955	0·2	0·2	—
	1956	—	—	—
Argentina	1955	208·5	14·8	55·0
	1956	246·7	21·8	65·6
Brazil	1955	5·6	—	10·1
	1956	24·3	0·3	—
Ecuador	1955–6	—	—	—
Colombia	1955	—	—	0·9
	1956	—	—	0·2
Former Belgian Congo	1955	—	—	1·1
	1956	—	—	1·1
Ghana	1955	—	—	0·1
	1956	—	—	0·1
Kenya	1955	0·2	1·5	3·7
	1956	0·5	1·9	3·3
Nigeria	1955	0·1	—	9·0
	1956	0·1	—	8·5
Fed. Rhodesia–Nyasaland	1955	3·7	0·1	2·7
	1956	2·2	0·2	2·3

TABLE VII—*continued*

Country	Year	Meat	Dairy products	Hides/Skins
Somali Republic	1955	—	0·4	1·2
	1956	0·1	0·2	1·1
Tanganyika	1955	1·4	—	3·5
	1956	1·0	0·1	3·4
Uganda	1955	—	—	1·9
	1956	—	—	2·2
Burma	1955	—	—	0·1
	1956	—	—	—
Ceylon	1955	—	—	0·1
	1956	—	—	—
Malaya–Singapore	1955	0·9	2·4	1·4
	1956	0·9	2·5	1·3
Thailand	1955	0·1	1·4	3·2
	1956	0·2	2·7	2·3
Indonesia	1955	—	—	1·5
	1956	—	—	1·6

* Based on F.A.O. Yearbook, 1957.

or herds. Here the presence of co-operative farmers of some education, substance and vision and of official livestock demonstration staff and centres might act as stimuli to the small farmers—but even this would necessitate an efficient extension service.

The present economic significance of livestock as an item of export is reasonably high in some countries (*vide* Table VII). The data, however, cannot illustrate the usage of the animals for draft, milk, meat, hide, mohair and other products. Furthermore, the traditional *prestige* significance, in many parts of Africa, of the ownership of a number of animals irrespective of their quality must be remembered.

In Africa and Asia there is a wide range of indigenous breeds, varieties and strains of cattle, sheep and goats, providing the sources of production. Within these or, at least, in certain of these breeds there is high potential for the selection and fixing of improved types capable of higher productivity, be this in flesh or, for cattle, in flesh and milk.

In Central and South America the naturalized livestock have excellent potential, this being particularly true of the European grade *criollo* cattle and some of the Corriedale, Merino, Romney Marsh and other breeds of sheep.

Exotic and naturalized livestock play a restricted but locally important rôle in montane Latin America* and parts of Africa and upland localities in Asia. According to the particular ecological setting and the breed and strain of animal, exotic livestock may suffer in varying degree from intolerance to humidity and heat, aridity and heat, pests and diseases, and from relative inefficiency in foraging for sustenance in the natural browse and pasturage. In some of the less severe sectors of Africa and Asia the grade animals (crosses of various proportions of exotic and indigenous blood) may prove to be adaptable and productive, where pure breeds are liable to respond poorly and even succumb to the rigours of the environment and to pests and disease.

Some of the special features of the indigenous breeds of cattle, sheep and goats in Africa and Asia deserve brief mention:

(*a*) their adaptability to the severity of the local conditions, be these warm and humid or hot and dry;

(*b*) their slow rate of maturation: six years for cattle; when better husbanded, four or five;

(*c*) their often relatively small dimensions and low weight—apart from certain well-known exceptions in cattle in subarid to arid West, Central and Southern Africa;

(*d*) their slow rate of breeding—and in the instance of poultry, the low fertility of eggs;

(*e*) the high mortality in calves and lambs;

(*f*) the small amount of milk produced, but its relatively high nutrient value;

(*g*) their local resistance to certain diseases—for example in parts of West Africa to local strains of trypanosomes responsible for animal trypanosomiasis;

(*h*) their common avoidance, instinctively, of toxic and other undesirable plants;

(*i*) their encouraging response to simple but reasonable husbandry: better feeding during the dry or cold season; ample supply of clean water, a modicum of routine veterinary attention, culling or castration of excess males, some protection against direct sunshine during the hottest hours in the hotter months and, in general, more able handling;

* Argentina, of course, leads the tropical world as an exporter of meat.

(*j*) where kraaling (enclosure) at night is avoidable because of the absence of preying carnivores, the ready response in condition to the additional material gained by night grazing and browsing.

Feeding trials in the three continents have demonstrated how excellent is the response of livestock to supplementary feeding during the dry and hot or the dry and cold seasons. In Latin America the naturalized higher grade exotic and the *criollo* cattle, in Africa the indigenous cattle, sheep and goats (in South Africa, Southern Rhodesia and upland Kenya, grade cattle of exotic-indigenous ancestry) and in Asia the indigenous cattle, put on good weight and condition when given sufficient supplementary fodder, water and salt. But while this essentially useful building up of livestock is of professional and economic interest it normally cannot be accomplished by the small pastoralist or farmer, because of the labour, the expense and, quite frequently, the sheer impossibility of growing or otherwise obtaining the fodder. Large and progressive owners in Latin America, South Africa, Southern Rhodesia, upland Kenya and upland Ceylon, however, are capable of growing, transporting and storing fodder and, accordingly, are able to maintain dairy and other better classes of livestock in fair to good condition and yield throughout the more severe seasons.

From demonstrations in various localities in the three continents the products derived from indigenous or naturalized livestock and, of course, from exotic grades where such are at ecological-physiological ease, always are improved appreciably by better husbandry and suitable veterinary care. In recent years it has been shown repeatedly over a wide range in the tropics and hotter subtropics that flesh, hides, skins, mohair and rough wool can be improved considerably in quality by the paying of simple attention to a relatively restricted number of prime points in management, slaughtering, quartering, flaying and so forth. While the supply of milk by indigenous cattle, sheep and goats rarely is much above the amount requisite for the raising of their off-spring, that additional amount nevertheless can be increased. Moreover, its more efficient conversion to cream or ghee can be accomplished through demonstration and consistent checking by the extension services. Were a sufficiently strong, capable and devoted service of this kind in existence in the main livestock-raising countries of the tropics and the hotter subtropics, the amount and the quality of all the animal products unquestionably could be raised greatly.

The need for the educating of the pastoralists in the regions under review is imperative, and this applies not only to the small pastoralists and to those who run livestock communally but also to a proportion of the farmers of foreign extraction in Latin America, South, Central and upland East Africa and upland Ceylon. Until a better concerted effort to do this over a wide range be exerted and a satisfactory standard of sound, practical demonstration and guidance be set, the husbandry and production of livestock owned by simple pastoralists must remain relatively inefficient over a considerable proportion of Latin America and much of Africa and Asia.

Bearing this in mind, it should be noted that in these days of widespread national aspiration to forge ahead with one form or another of agricultural development, some administrations both 'new' and much older—as in Latin America—are showing an increasing anxiety to expand the livestock industry. This has been noted over a wide span of the tropics and will continue to show itself. Most of the proposed projects are either official or quasi-official as to concept, funds and personnel. Most of the proposals could not bear an acute analysis of their professional, managerial and economic features. A common characteristic is the apparent failure of the politicians—so often behind the proposals—to realize that the establishment of flocks and herds and their appropriate selection, breeding, husbandry, management, health and disposal cannot be ensured merely by the passing of resolutions and the provision of capital, imprest and goodwill.

The difference between a venture in livestock development and the building of a factory or a mill for a specific enterprise, in which the raw products are assured, does not often obtrude itself sufficiently clearly in the deliberations about the large-scale raising of animals. Advisers in underdeveloped countries accordingly must exhibit more than the ordinary understanding, tact and professional integrity in saying exactly what they believe should be said about grandiose propositions born with the germ of failure strong within them.

(III) Animal Health

Although the state of animal health services still is far from satisfactory in many parts of the tropics and hotter subtropics there has been a marked improvement in these since 1945. This is especially true of many countries in Africa and of some in Asia, while in Latin

America there also has been a fair degree of expansion and of increased efficiency. Should the rate of increased coverage and of enhanced efficiency continue for several decades, even at the rates of the past fifteen years, the effect upon the general vigour of the livestock populations of the three continents should be marked. Indeed by then it well might be argued, with justification, that veterinary services and animal husbandry have so grown in efficiency as to raise the bogey of the risk of a superabundance of domesticated animals in due time. Premature death shortly will have been reduced to such an extent as to render untrue the old view that in the tropics and hotter subtropics the premature mortality always would be sufficiently great to counteract the risk of an excess of livestock in any particular country.*

A brief summary of some of the more significant pests and diseases of livestock in the three continents follows:

Some Important Vectors of Disease

Ixodidae and Argasidae (ticks) and Diptera (including midges, mosquitoes, flies of diverse kinds and, in Africa, that most important fly, the Tsetse (*Glossina* spp.).

Some Important Parasites

Serious endoparasites exist in the form of nematodes, platyhelminths, trematodes and cestodes, while ecoparasitic mites and ticks cause much irritation.

Disease-bearing Viruses and Rickettsias

Rinderpest in various parts of Africa, in indigenous antelopes and bovines, and occurring also in India and Burma and with a history of earlier very restricted occurrence in Brazil and the Philippines; *foot-and-mouth* disease in cattle, and to a lesser extent in pigs, in many parts of Africa and in South America; *rabies*, widely spread, the carriers being *Viveridae, Herpestinae, Sciuridae, Felidae* and *Mustelidae; Swine-fever*, perhaps indigenous to America, occurring in South-Eastern Africa, indigenous porcines being susceptible:

---

* The proposal by various international bodies that game should be 'farmed' in certain marginal areas in Africa, probably will call for strictures by veterinarians, because of the related risk of pest and disease transmission to domesticated animals.

Potamochoerus and *Phacochoerus*, and thus potentially dangerous as transmitters; *Three Days' Sickness*, common in India and Southern Africa; *Heartwater*, in South and Central Africa, South-West Africa, the former Belgian Congo and West Africa, in cattle, sheep and goats; *Blue Tongue* in sheep, Africa; *African Horse-sickness* in South, East and Central Africa and Eritrea.

Disease-bearing Bacteria

Anthrax in all classes of livestock, cosmopolitan and sporadic; *Bang's Disease* or contagious abortion, widespread in cattle; *Tuberculosis* in all classes of livestock, cosmopolitan; *Johne's Disease* in cattle in India and Southern Africa; *Actinomycosis*, *Dermatomycosis*, in cattle and pigs, widespread; *Epizootic Lymphangitis* in Africa, India and the Philippines; *Pleuropneumonia* or lung-sickness in cattle, in Africa, Central Asia and India; *Mastitis* in cattle, widespread; *Calf Paratyphoid* due to *Salmonella* spp. in cattle, ducks and humans, in South America, Africa and India; *Swine Erysipelas* in Africa and India; *Blackquarter* (Quarter-evil, Blackleg) due to *Clostridium chauvoei*, the 'most widespread and important anaerobe affecting animals' (Henning, 1956), world-wide; *Botulism* —Bone-craving, Osteophagia, 'Pica'—Africa; *Tetanus* or lock-jaw, widespread.

Protozoan-induced Diseases

Bovine Piroplasmosis, Texas fever, Central and South America ('La Tristeza'), Africa, Indonesia and various other parts of Asia; *Anaplasmosis*, gall-sickness, South America, Africa, Asia; *East Coast Fever* (Theilerioses), cattle, Africa in Eastern and Southern sectors; *Biliary Fever* of horses—*Equine Piroplasmosis*—Central and South America, Southern Africa, India and the Philippines; *Trypanosomiasis*: (*a*) *Nagana*, in three-fifths of tropical Africa, all domesticated animals, the reservoir of *Trypanosomes* being the blood of game mammals, birds and reptiles; *Trypanosoma congolense*, *T. brucei* and *T. vivax* (human sleeping-sickness: *T. gambiense* and *T. rhodesiense*); (*b*) *Dourine*, due to *T. equiperdum*, parts of Africa and Asia, in horses.

International organizations (F.A.O. in all the continents and the International Bureau for Epidemological Diseases (I.B.E.D.) in Africa are examples) are making valuable contributions toward research and extension in veterinary medicine.

CHAPTER VI

Forest Conservation and Management

Objective

Although it is necessary to refer occasionally to the use of the forest regions proper—mainly the HHF: highly humid, the HF: humid, and the HMF: humid montane forests—for agricultural purposes, my objective rather is to discuss briefly the outstanding features of the *pattern, problems and promise* of these regions in terms of the conservation of water and soil for which they are responsible, the products they yield and the management they either receive or deserve. While certain *wooded savanna* regions— especially the SHWS: subhumid wooded savanna and to a less extent the SAWS: subarid wooded savanna—yield some timber, resins and other products, these so-called 'open' forests or wood-lands and the open woodlands are not covered here.

Except for swamp, riverine and periodically inundated types con-ditioned by the master physical factors, moisture, aeration and drainage, the forests mentioned in this discussion lie within the definition given in Chapter III: Forest of highly humid, humid, humid-subhumid types at low and medium and montane elevations in the tropics and hotter subtropics; normally evergreen to mixed evergreen and deciduous vegetation; trees 60 to 200 feet high, with the crowns normally touching, overlapping and in stratification so as to form a closed or almost closed canopy; soils normally with more litter, raw organic matter and incorporated organic matter and available nitrogen than any of the less densely canopied vegetation communities; *climax* but with an increasing proportion of *secondary* vegetation due to exploitation for timber and to 'shifting' and 'sedentary cultivation'.

FOREST CONSERVATION AND MANAGEMENT

Background

Because the subject of the forest resources of the tropics and sub-tropics is covered in summary form in two recent books (F.A.O. (1955) and Haden-Guest, Wright and Teclaff (1956)), and as Richards earlier (1952) discussed the nature and structure of tropical forests, I do not attempt to cover these topics.

In considering information brought together by F.A.O. (1955) and Haden-Guest *et al.* (1956) it should be remembered that owing to the nature of the information available to the compilers it was impossible to differentiate satisfactorily between true forest and wooded savanna and related types, and between the two functional types of forest proper—that best suited for protection of water and soil and that of economic value for timber and other production. Furthermore it is often difficult to differentiate between tropical and subtropical forests because of the lack of descriptive data as to elevation, terrain, temperature and rainfall. Another feature complicating the gaining of a clearer impression of the nature of the forest resources is that the proportion of exploited or 'broken' forest, either in the form of forest subjected to 'shifting cultivation' or, very rarely, reserved for the regeneration of economic timber, is not known in many instances. In any case, the relevant facts only very occasionally are recorded.

With these reservations, therefore, I note some details of forest distribution and selected resources from the summary by F.A.O. (1955).

(1) Distribution of the World's Forests

For the sake of obtaining a very broad impression of the relative proportions of tropical and subtropical forest to those of the temperate regions, I draw attention to the data in Table VIII.

(2) Roughly Estimated Percentage of Accessible Forests and Forests in Use in Proportion to the Total Forest Area in each Region

Table IX gives the *percentage* of accessible forests and of those in use, based on the *total forest area* of the regions (F.A.O., 1955). The percentage of *inaccessible* forest is derived by subtraction.

Some rough impression of the proportions of unexploited accessible forest to that now in use is gained from data selected from F.A.O. (1955):

FOREST CONSERVATION AND MANAGEMENT

TABLE VIII

DISTRIBUTION OF THE WORLD'S FORESTS AND THE ROUGH PROPORTIONS OF BROAD-
LEAFED AND CONIFEROUS TYPES AND THEIR ACCESSIBILITY

(millions of hectares)

Region	Forests			Broad-leafed	Coni-ferous	Percentage of World Area
	Total	Inacces-sible	Acces-sible			
Europe	136	3	133	57	79	3·5
U.S.S.R.	743	318	425	163	580	19·4
Alaska, Canada and U.S.A.	656	344	312	193	463	17·1
Central and South America	890	561	329	863	27	23·2
Africa	801	517	284	798	3	20·9*
Asia	525	214	311	405	120	13·7
Pacific	86	66	20	78	8	2·2
Total	3837	2063	1814	2557	1280	100·0

* Too great, because non-forest vegetation is included: wooded savanna and scrub.

TABLE IX

PROPORTION OF ACCESSIBLE TO INACCESSIBLE FORESTS

Region	Forests		Inaccessible by inference
	Accessible (percentage)	In use (percentage)	
Europe	98	96	2
U.S.S.R.	57	47	43
Alaska, Canada and U.S.A.	48	34	52
Central and South America	37	9	63
Africa	35	13	65†
Asia	59	44	41
Pacific	23	20	77
World	47	30	53

† Too great, for the reason given in the footnote to Table VIII.

121

TABLE X

UNEXPLOITED ACCESSIBLE FORESTS IN CONTRAST TO THOSE IN USE FOR SELECTED
COUNTRIES IN TROPICS AND HOTTER SUBTROPICS

(in thousands of hectares)

Territory	Accessible forests	
	In use at present	As yet unexploited
Argentina	10,000	50,000
Brazil	30,010	90,040
Colombia	410	61,590
Ecuador	500	2000
Mexico	4500	20,060
Peru	5000	10,000
Former Belgian Congo	5300	9700
Former French Equatorial Africa	12,030	15,020
Former French West Africa	10,500	3500

(3) Ownership of Accessible Forests

According to F.A.O. (1955) the ownership of the *accessible* forests is roughly as set out in Table XI:

TABLE XI

OWNERSHIP OF ACCESSIBLE FORESTS, TROPICS AND SUBTROPICS: EXPRESSED AS
PERCENTAGES

Region	Forms of ownership		
	State	Communal (including Tribal)	Private
Central and South America	58	6	36
Africa	74	23	3
Asia	72	18	10
Pacific	76	—	24

The relatively high proportion of *communally owned* forest in Africa and Asia is noteworthy—due to the inclusion of Tribal—or in West Africa, Stool—land under forest.

122

FOREST CONSERVATION AND MANAGEMENT

(4) Forest Area per Capita

Although the data derived by F.A.O. (1955) obviously are crude because of the various uncertainties in their collection, or rather estimation, and in the interpretation that may be drawn from them, the following selected figures give a very rough *indication* of the *total* area, the area of *accessible* forest and the area of forest actually in use *per capita:*

TABLE XII

ROUGH INDICATIONS OF THE FOREST AREA PER CAPITA: TOTAL, ACCESSIBLE FOREST
AND FOREST IN USE FOR THE TROPICS AND SUBTROPICS

(hectares per capita)

Region	Total area	Area accessible	Area in use
Central and South America	5·2	1·9	0·5
Africa	3·9	1·4	0·5
Asia	0·4	0·2	0·2
Pacific	6·7	1·6	1·3
World	1·6	0·7	0·5

In much of Africa, parts of Latin America, parts of Asia and parts of the Pacific the hectares *per capita* are of major significance in that they throw light upon the potential and the actual proportions of forest available for 'shifting' and 'sedentary cultivation'. The figures are rendered less valuable by the fact that often vegetation other than true forest is included in the regional totals. Glaring examples are Bechuanaland, the Rhodesias and South-West Africa, where virtually no *true* forest of any significance occurs, but which are credited with a very large to large *per capita* hectarage! *Wooded savanna* I do not consider as *forest*.

(5) Proportion of Reserved and Non-reserved Forest

In terms of gazetted areas set aside specifically for conservation and skilled forest management the areas of *reserved* forest in the tropics and subtropics still is relatively low, despite efforts made by the one-time Colonial powers in parts of Africa and Asia. For what they are worth, the following data abstracted from F.A.O. (1955) give some indication of the position in the regions concerned, in terms of *accessible* forest:

123

FOREST CONSERVATION AND MANAGEMENT

TABLE XIII

RESERVED AND NON-RESERVED PROPORTIONS OF ACCESSIBLE FOREST IN THE TROPICS
AND SUBTROPICS

(millions of hectares)

Region	Reserved	Not reserved	Comment
Central and South America	1	39	Data based on a response for information: 12% only
Africa	83	97	63% response
Asia	84	60	46% response
Pacific	8	8	80% response

Without entering into details it can be said that the proportions of reserved to total forest area in tropical countries is from nil or negligible to relatively high: up to 20 to 25 per cent of true forest. The generalization by F.A.O. (1955), based on responses by governments regarding 815 million hectares of accessible forest, that in Asia and Africa about half the accessible stands were reserved to date, would need detailed explanation in light of the precise definitions of reserved and accessible forest. To me the figure seems too high. Conversely, the generalization that in Latin America the progress in the establishment of reserves has been negligible is undoubtedly correct. Both in Africa and Asia scope exists for more vigorous action in the establishment of further reserves, but in Latin America this practice scarcely has been commenced.

(6) Management and Exploitation Practices

A study of Table XIV—based on F.A.O. (1955)—reveals the relatively low standards of management and exploitation existing in the tropics and subtropics. Notable exceptions are found in Pakistan, India, Malaya, the former and the present British Territories in Africa (Ghana, Nigeria, Tanganyika), Kenya, Union of South Africa and several former French territories (Guinea, Ivory Coast, Gabon).

Noteworthy are the very unsatisfactory conditions existing in Latin America, the only slightly less unsatisfactory ones in Africa, the relatively good ones in Asia—due to the boost given in Pakistan, India and Malaya—and the seemingly very good ones in the Pacific due very largely to the conditions holding in Australia. Much weight

TABLE XIV

MANAGEMENT AND EXPLOITATION PRACTICES IN THE TROPICS AND SUBTROPICS
(millions of hectares and percentage)

Region	Area of forests under working plans	Percentage of such forests in the areas in use	Estimated percentage area subject to felling practices as described		
			Good	Fair	Poor and destructive
Central and South America	6	6	10	30	60
Africa	12	13	10	30	60
Asia	52	25	25	50	25
Pacific	9	54	60	15	25

should not be placed upon these data, but broadly they do illustrate the conditions mentioned. By contrast, the percentage of the three felling practices recorded for Europe are 60 per cent good, 35 per cent fair and only 5 per cent poor or destructive. Clearly the tropics and subtropics, except for the countries mentioned in the first paragraph, have to go far before reaching this standard.

Pattern

Against the background described it is obvious that the tropical and subtropical forest regions cover a slightly larger area even than the great temperate ones: about 60 per cent of the world's forest area; Central and South America with almost a quarter, Africa with about one-fifth and Asia with about one-seventh of the world's total hectarage. The vast proportion of the forests of these continents is tropical, a relatively small proportion montane and subtropical. Broad-leafed forests constitute about 93 per cent of the hectarage, the coniferous occurring mainly but not entirely in the montane and subtropical sectors.

Inaccessibility still is a common feature: compared with a world forest area inaccessibility percentage of about 53 that of the tropics and subtropics is about 61. Ownership is mainly State—the range being from about 60 per cent in Latin America to about 75 per cent in Africa—communally or tribally owned forest being extensive in

Africa (about 23 per cent) but less so in Asia (about 18 per cent). Although these figures should not be rated too highly the area of forest *per capita* is instructive: 7 hectares in the Pacific, about 6 hectares in Latin America, 3 hectares in Africa and as little as 0·4 hectare in Asia.

Excluding some special types such as the coniferous and the swamp forests, many of the tropical and subtropical forests have much in common. They are evergreen to mixed evergreen-and-deciduous, with dense canopy and three to four or more strata or layers: the emergents, the main true top canopy trees, the trees of the third layer, and one or more layers of smaller trees, and then tall shrubs and the ground flora. Tree ferns may occur locally in some types. The soils contain organic matter of higher content than elsewhere while plant nutrient content is moderate to high, but is evanescent when cropped and on the introduction of excessive insolation and direct rainfall. Almost invariably the soils are highly erodible. Owing to the highly humid to humid to humid-subhumid climate—varying with the subregion—and the relatively high and monotonous temperatures, the rate of regrowth from seed, coppice and 'suckers' is remarkably luxuriant and rapid. An early re-vegetating is normal on sites deprived of their cover by exploitation, fire, cultivation and any other cause.

In the bioclimatic classification outlined in Chapter III the major forest regions and variants are brought together, the principal being the highly humid (HHF), the humid (HF), the humid montane (HMF) forests and the subtropical variants.

The present educational level of the great majority of those who live either directly or indirectly through the forests—as cultivators, farmers and forest workers—is usually low. Inaccessibility, inefficient communications even in the more accessible localities, absence or insufficiency of the simpler facilities for elementary education and, sometimes, local poverty, militate against the rapid raising of the standards of education and living. To this is attributable in part the frequent absence of a spirit of interest in the forest peoples in the conservation and the improvement of the forest in and upon which they live. But it must be remembered also that these people depend upon the local clearing or thinning of the forest for the winning of their sustenance by cropping and, locally, by the holding of small livestock. It is a moot point, therefore, whether the forest is considered a traditional enemy or a heritage: some forms of behaviour suggest the one, others the opposite. It would be wrong, of course, to conclude that the simple, uneducated forest dwellers do not possess a certain inherited store of forest lore and knowledge, inevitably unscientific but nevertheless invaluable for casting light upon some matters that scientific research has not had opportunity yet to explain. My own experience in South, East and West Africa teaches me that the forest dwellers know much that science as yet cannot explain.

Because of my supposition that those who have lived for many generations in and upon the forests could be led to work for their more effective conservation and improvement, I still am not without hope that the forests yet can be saved from deterioration.

The history of the tropical and subtropical forests in the three continents indicates that indigenous and expatriate men alike have for centuries instinctively turned their hands against the forests—because of the needs of the cultivator, because of the timber and other requirements of urban communities, and because of the official demand for revenue to be won by sale and possibly export of timber and other products. The recalling of the nature of the tropics-wide practice of traditional 'shifting cultivation' and of the commonly wasteful exploitation of timber is sufficient to define the rôles played by men both relatively simple and somewhat more educated but often more grasping.

It would be difficult to put a reliable figure to the percentage of forest that has been either destroyed almost beyond recognition or has been converted into a medley of *secondary* types, from 'false' desert and open grassland to 'broken' or farm forest. According to the country and district this may be from a low to a very high proportion of the total original hectarage: from a few to as much as 90 per cent. Fortunately the ecological truth of the old saying 'where once a forest has been a forest could come again—given the chance' is borne out very often. Only rarely are the local climatic and the soil conditions altered so fundamentally as to make this rehabilitation impossible within a reasonable period.

From the angle of the professional forester—for the greater part still trained against the background of *temperate* forests and the related art and science of forestry—the tropical and subtropical forests possess many impressive features. They are rarely constituted by extensive pure stands or stands of several main species only, but usually exist as communities rich in species. Their biology—species by species—and the ecology of the natural communities comprising them still have not been investigated, except locally and superficially. While much still must be learned about the nature and the way of life of temperate forests—even of planted stands of single species —our ignorance of the much more complex forest communities of the tropics and subtropics is abysmal by comparison.

If the silviculturist be beset by problems in the selection of species and of individuals for either retention or removal, and in regenerating, with selected species, the forests worked according to the tenets of the 'selection system' modified to suit the local conditions, the mind of the economist is as much befogged by the puzzles presented by the warring demands of silviculture and finance. While the silviculturist, with complete professional justification, might wish to convert a community of many species to one of several particularly valuable ones, the costs of the operation might be insurmountable because of there being no sale for the species to be reduced or practically eliminated. The helpful operation of assisting promising large but immature trees of chosen kinds by the removal of boles of unwanted kinds and by the slashing of tangles of lianas or monkey-ropes may cost £1 to £5 per acre. As the return from that acre is nil or negligible for 20 to 50 or more years, the cost of the improvement operations, at interest, becomes a millstone around the neck of the silviculturist mindful of economics.

Apart from occasional exceptions the yields of utilizable timber from saleable trees of the requisite dimensions and quality are relatively low per hectare. This is because of the restricted number of individuals of appropriate size and quality which could be removed without damaging the canopy, the regeneration, and the soil. As already mentioned, forest soils deteriorate physically, in fertility and biologically when exposed to severe isolation and direct rainfall, hence the canopy should not be removed or heavily thinned except very locally and for a restricted time—a few weeks to a few months only.

Forest mensuration in the tropics and subtropics reveals that the mean annual girth increment, at the standard height, often is small to moderate in the valuable species of tree: the utilizable minimum girth limits rarely being attained under 60 to 80 years in the tropics, and in the montane and subtropical variants frequently not under 100 to 180 years. In some species, however, the increment is rapid when compared with that of hardwoods in the temperate region.

FOREST CONSERVATION AND MANAGEMENT

Wastage in the exploitation of the indigenous forests is great, especially in those far removed from centres of conversion and where the supervision necessarily is lax. As much as 25 to 75 per cent of the bole and better crown wood may be left to rot in the forest. A further proportion often is lost through careless felling of the wanted trees upon those not selected for exploitation. Saplings, poles and immature trees of various dimensions thus are destroyed or injured. Inefficient planning of exploitation also results in valuable timber being left too long in the forest, with consequential serious deterioration if not complete loss.

Ignoring marked exceptions according to the species and the locality, the regeneration stages frequently are reasonably well represented in the height and the diameter classes, rendering seeding and planting unnecessary. In some localities, however, sowings and plantings are necessary, this occasionally being done by means of the *taungya* system. By this arrangement cultivators are permitted to crop a certain portion of thinned or exploited forest for a season or more, provided they establish by an agreed date and tend for a time, either gratis or for a slight payment, an agreed number of young trees. This procedure is worthy of application in many parts of the tropics where cultivators inhabit the forests.

The healing of the gaps in the canopy caused by the felling and the exploitation of timber usually is accomplished rapidly by means of woody shrubs and trees of pioneer kind, which form communities under which the economic species later establish themselves. Where pioneer or 'nurse' communities are absent, however, the *secondary* succession is marked by rampant grasses and tall annual or perennial herbs and subshrubs, which do not permit the establishment of forest regeneration until they themselves are ousted by taller growth after about five to ten years.

* Exploitation in some countries—and notably in those formerly or still under British and French influence—is suitably controlled, either in special *concessions* or under the supervision of forestry staff in forest *reserves*. This entails a minimum girth class control, below which trees in the *concessions* may not be felled. In the forest *reserves* a much closer adherence to regulations is enforced so as to ensure that silvicultural requirements are met as well as possible under the prevailing circumstances. In other countries—and this covers the greater proportion of the tropics of Latin America, Africa and some parts of Asia—there is little if any control of exploitation. As a result

the forests are soon destroyed or very much impaired in value as potential sources of timber in the decades ahead. Fortunately still fairly extensive areas exist in South America and parts of Africa—both accessible and inaccessible—which could be saved from feckless exploitation. But this will not happen unless the local administrations are induced to practise sound conservation and management. It is hoped that the 1960 World Forestry Conference in Seattle will succeed in stimulating certain governments—especially in Latin America and Africa—to be more mindful of their priceless and irreplaceable forest heritage.

In some countries in the three continents little if any sense of the significance of their forests exists in the minds of the nationals and their political leaders. Except for some excellent forestry officials there is no understanding of a national responsibility for the protection and welfare of the forests, so as to ensure their continued utilization and maintenance. It is usually only after forests have been ruined, or well nigh so, that either the administrations or the more public spirited and intelligent nationals begin to realize that something should be done to preserve and to add to the forest estate.

The lively interest being shown in the opening of forest for *colonization* in parts of South America and South-East Asia—as in Peru, Ceylon and Malaya—suggests that conservation and management either might fail to be applied by some governments or might suffer where already applied by others, in their anxiety to expand agriculture at the highest possible tempo. I do not doubt that in some parts of Africa, either already politically free or shortly to become so, a similar desire to assist cultivators to produce more food and commodity crops will speed the destruction of the forests.

Where indigenous forests regenerate poorly and grow too slowly for economic purposes, or where the kinds of local timber are deemed unsuitable for local use and for export, there is a tendency to look to *exotics* for the provision of more rapidly growing and more suitable timbers. In the subtropics—notably in Southern Africa—and in *montane* localities in the tropics—as in Kenya—there is every indication that this is a wise policy: Mexican, Caribbean and other thermophilic pines and Eucalypts being the most appropriate species in these subregions. The introduction of exotics into indigenous forest in the low and medium elevations in the tropics, however, rarely if ever has succeeded except very locally. This is not to argue that ultimately some measure of success might not be gained through research and trial plantings, but rather to suggest that paying more intensive attention to the improvement of the forests by means of the indigenous species themselves is likely to lead more rapidly to practical progress.

Problems

Among the many problems presented by the tropical and subtropical forests the following merit special thought:

Satisfactory methods must be derived for forest conservation, compatible with the economy of the particular country. All conservation is expensive, but there are degrees of intensity of conservation and therefore of the corresponding costs. The particular policies and practices decided, country by country, must depend upon: (1) The extent of the forests, their shape and their physiographic setting. (2) Their relative vulnerability to lightning, fire, 'shifting' and 'sedentary' cultivation, grazing and browsing by cattle, sheep and goats and rooting by pigs. (3) Theft of large timber and minor products. (4) General traditional attitude of the local community— whether the forests be of some public account or not. (5) The proximity of fire-resistant or fire-vulnerable vegetation such as forest relics, secondary grassland or wooded savanna and subhumid wooded savanna.

Where *no* reserves have been created for the conservation and the silvicultural management of the forests, the winning of the support of the administration and the recognition by the local communities of the value to the nation of these must be faced wisely and courageously. It might prove also that the addition of further reserves to those already existing is almost as refractory a task as the establishment of reserves for the first time. Experience shows that it may be wise not to over-bid for reserves, but rather to gain these gradually, through a sound practical demonstration of technical and economic principles.

Where reserves contain even a minimum of agricultural crops— as for example fruit trees, coffee, cocoa, rubber, cola and oil-palm —the difficulty of the 'new' administrations in restricting the activities of the cultivators usually is great. It is commonly easier for an administration to yield to the public demand for the expansion of planted areas in reserves than to insist upon either definite restriction or ultimate, planned withdrawal of the cultivators.

Silviculturally, the gradual conversion of the mixed forests to stands richer in the economically more important species is perhaps the most difficult problem for solution. Relatively little practical progress has been made except on very small experimental areas. Here indeed is a challenge to foresters both foreign and national. Admittedly the economic value of the forests must remain far less than need be, so long as either the complex mixture of a few economically valuable species with a much larger number of non-utilizable ones remains the common feature, or until some economic use be found for these 'other' species. Much study of technical and economic nature awaits students of forest utilization and the timber trade.

The reduction in the number of constituent timber species apart, the forests raise many silvicultural-ecological questions in natural or artificial regeneration. These include the rehabilitation of gaps torn in the canopy during exploitation; the possible use of selected *exotics* either as nurses or for timber; and the maintenance of the chemico-physico-biotic characteristics of the soils. Insolation and the effect of heavy direct rain cause serious deterioration of the soil, hence the exploitation, silvicultural thinnings and cleanings (*nettoiement*) must be regulated so as to expose the soils as little as possible.

Even if the excess of unwanted species be reduced by means which prove to be economic, the leading of the forest of one or several species of saleable kind toward what foresters consider to be a *normal** stocking of the major *size* classes will be no easy matter. The *age* classes of classical temperate planted forests cannot be parallelled in the indigenous tropical/subtropical stands. Fundamentally important considerations such as thinning, cleaning, increase or decrease of regeneration of various *size* groups, and the length of the rotation for attaining a minimum economic girth for long will puzzle the professional forester, who at the same time must keep a wary eye upon the economics of production.

Where the richly mixed forests must be led toward a simpler composition of several economic species every effort should be exerted to alter simultaneously the complexity of the *secondary* vegetation, which heals up raw spots on the ground and gaps in the canopy caused during exploitation. It might be found that some suitable useful indigenous or exotic species grown in appropriate density could take the place of the plethora of *secondary* indigenous

* The classical concept of the *normally* stocked forest is applicable in systematic forestry in parts of Europe, but is meaningless in the mixed indigenous forests of the tropics and subtropics.

species usually occurring in the successional stages after fellings. In areas under 'shifting cultivation' this possibility of improving the fertility and the physical features of the soils planted to annual crops is worthy of serious investigation. A solution through establishing one or two readily assertive species—whether saleable or not—might be of great potential economic significance both to the cultivator and the silviculturist. The cultivators responsible for the establishment of forest trees on a *taungya* basis could benefit greatly by the use of artificially established species, were these to accelerate and intensify the action of the nutrient cycle of chemical foods. (*Vide* Greenland and Kowal (1959), Phillips (1959B), Nye (1960) and the literature therein cited for an account of this cycle in the forest—whereby the trees return to the surface the nutrients brought from the various depths; *vide* also Kellogg and Davol (1949) for the former Belgian Congo.)

Nowhere in the tropics and subtropics is the necessity for the maintenance of the *biotic balance* or *equilibrium* more inportant than in the forests. This should be a guiding principle in forest conservation, exploitation, regeneration, conversion to 'shifting' or 'sedentary' cropping, wild life management within the forest and all other relevant activities.

Unfortunately the extraction and utilization of the products of the tropical and subtropical indigenous forests are still primitive and wasteful. The overcoming of some of the greater difficulties is urgently required. All the operations are involved: mechanized felling and directing of fall of the tree, its conversion to the requisite first dimensions or trade cuts *in situ*, its loading and transporting to the mill. There is much scope also for the improvement of seasoning of tropical timbers and the better preparation of a wide range of minor forest products—gums, resins, oils, latexes and the like. Special technical difficulties abound, the overcoming of which could help toward stimulating the economy.

At the risk of being criticized for repetition I reiterate the necessity for the investigation of the potentialities of well-selected *exotic* timber trees, particularly where the indigenous forests either have been destroyed or very seriously disturbed. At the higher elevations and in the subtropical subregions every effort should be exerted to find suitable *soft* woods (for example *Pinus* spp. from the Caribbean, Mexican and similar subregions) for extensive establishment.

Fortunately there is usually not the antagonism between agriculture and forestry in the tropics and subtropics that pervades the temperate and more progressive countries—perhaps because the cultivator lives in and depends upon the forest. But the existing harmonious interrelations must be watched so that these do not deteriorate through any influence, including that of expatriate forestry and agricultural advisers not *au fait* with the local sociological conditions. The harmonious interplay of both these great arts and in-industries is so essential to mutual progress that very special attention should be directed toward the solution of all apparent reciprocal irritations as soon as these appear.

I was much impressed at the clear understanding of the Forest Department, Malaya, when the future implications of a much expanded agriculture in parts of the country clearly indicated the planned reduction of the forests within certain districts. The necessity for such a planned retreat was appreciated by the Department, which made useful proposals about ways and means for bringing this about with the least possible loss to the nation. Where such happy understanding does not exist, however, the task of evolving agreed bases for future planning could be formidable, and for this very reason should be faced in good time.

Promise

The outstanding *promise* for the future of tropical and subtropical forestry is the still untouched wealth of the South American countries, and notably in Brazil, Peru, Argentina and Chile. Provided these vast areas as yet untouched—largely because of their inaccessibility for the extraction of timber—are suitably divided for development and those portions set aside for *reserves* and *timber concessions* are administered and managed wisely, they should yield well in the future.

In Africa the better portions of the highly humid forest (HHF) and the humid forest (HF) in the Congo Republic (former Belgian Congo) deserve further demarcation and reservation. It is hoped that the new African administration or administrations—against the background of what the Belgian authorities taught—will look upon the country's forests as a national heritage and upon their wise management as a sacred trust. If this be not so, the devastation of forest still relatively unspoiled could follow within several decades. It behoves other administrations—Nigeria, Ghana, the Ivory Coast, the Gabon, Tanganyika and Kenya more particularly—to see that the possession of political power is accompanied by an increased sense of responsibility toward the forest reserves and other areas previously set aside by the British and the French for systematic exploitation and management. The forests may show promise but it depends upon the governments whether that promise ever can be fulfilled. Casual administration, the opening of reserves for uncontrolled exploitation and the weakening or dissolution of the existing forest services could do irreparable harm.

One feature promising well for the continuity of the forests is the frequency of fair to good natural regeneration. In Central and South America, in Africa and in Asia the natural regeneration of the economic species, according to the type of forest and locality, is either fairly or very good. There are examples to the contrary, of course, where for one reason or another the regeneration is either absent or sparse and unpromising. Poor regeneration occurs in highly humid, humid and humid-subhumid forests alike, being caused by a variety of phenomena including poor fertilization of the flowers, small fruit and seed crops, pests, diseases, local weather conditions and excessively wet or dry soil conditions at critical phases. Density of canopy and severe competition for moisture by the constituents of the forest naturally contribute.

Slowly but surely a store of knowledge about the silviculture and management of the tropical and subtropical forests is being accumulated, knowledge of the kind that fifty years ago scarcely existed outside the Indian Forest Service. Today, elsewhere in Asia and in various parts of Africa valuable local knowledge is available. Perhaps because of her vast forest resources South America has been less active in learning about her forest wealth, while the same could be said of Central America—except for Mexico. But there are signs, even if still few and faint, that a change is dawning in the attitude of the various administrations toward this most important of natural resources, the forests of the subcontinent. Guided by the splendid examples of India and Pakistan in following the policies and practices initiated by Dietrich Brandis a century ago, other Asian countries might either continue the good work commenced—as in Ceylon and Malaya—or blaze new trails in conservation and silviculture.

A feature, promising well for the future, is the increasing number of the nationals of tropical countries who are studying forestry at several levels. This should engender the ferment of greater interest in the territorial forests by both the administrations and the departments concerned.

There is still a tendency for some of the countries more experienced in forestry to send some of their men to study in British and European or American University Departments of Forestry. While this has the disadvantage of there being an inclination in these Universities to teach temperate forestry in too much detail to men who do not require this knowledge, there is the merit that a widening in outlook often develops in students who spend a period abroad. To develop good local schools of forestry, at higher and lower levels, is a useful step toward acquiring information about tropical-subtropical forestry, its problems and promise.

Fortunately the Food and Agriculture Organization (F.A.O.) shows an interest in the forests of the tropics and subtropics, from conservation, management and exploitation at the one end to education and research at the other. The United States Operations Mission (U.S.O.M.) and the United States Department of Agriculture: Foreign Agricultural Service (U.S.D.A.: F.A.S.) also are stimulating interest in forestry, especially in Latin America. The inter-African organization, C.C.T.A./C.S.A., is pressing the need for the investigation of forestry problems. In Asia the Colombo Plan is paying attention to the advancement of forestry, through the efforts of some of its member countries.

Recent study of the mixed tropical hardwoods of Africa and elsewhere has stimulated the hope that these might be used for pulping. Should this be so there would be immediate justification for the introduction of silvicultural improvement fellings in forests over-rich in species at present of no other known commercial value. These then could be thinned, so as to encourage the development of a few chosen species of more than ordinary value.

Encouraging as the foregoing may appear as a promise for the future, it should be remembered that nothing can help to fulfil this promise other than wise statesmanship, sound legislation, efficient technical services, educating of the forest-dwelling communities, enlightenment of the converters of timber and other forest products and the opening of areas still inaccessible. As the forces of inertia and wastefulness are strong indeed, they could cause the very rapid deterioration in area and in quality of the forest estate in many underdeveloped tropical countries.

But foresters are well accustomed to steady battling for their professional ideals—and it is certain that there is an abundant *promise* of opportunities for more and very strenuous battling in the coming years.

CHAPTER VII

Conservation of Soil, Water and the Biotic Balance

There is an increasing necessity in the tropics and the hotter subtropics for the principles and practices of *conservation* of vegetation, soil and water to be understood more clearly than at present, and for the application of these by the administrations, the cultivators and the pastoralists.

Closely interlinked with this is the really urgent further requirement that, in the interests of both sentiment and economics, the *biotic interrelations* of plants, animals wild and domesticated, man and the environment should be appreciated in order that these are disturbed as little as possible. Not only does this intimate association of life and environment bear upon the selection, maintenance and management of Nature reserves but also is of fundamental importance throughout the whole gamut of agriculture, forestry and related human activities.

(I) Conservation of Vegetation, Soil and Water

Since the last war government and other interests in many parts of the tropics and subtropics have given some attention to both the positive and the negative aspects of the conservation of vegetation, soil and water. This is worthy of note because some of these self-same governments earlier did not always appear to realize the necessity for the taking of steps to prevent or to reduce the deterioration of these basic natural resources.

Although education, demonstration and propaganda in the United States had aroused the interest of agriculturists, foresters, educationists, district commissioners and progressive farmers in various parts of Africa, in India, Ceylon and Malaya, the lessons of her experience did not impress the senior members of the various administrations as having a message for them, the rank and file of their public services and the local farming communities. General Smuts himself had written and spoken vigorously since 1925 on the subject of deterioration of these resources in South, Central and

East Africa and had inaugurated a better concerted official action in his own country in 1932, but it is doubtful whether his warnings ever penetrated much beyond Africa south of the equator.

Partly because of the travelling of numerous Americans to many countries hitherto unknown to them, partly because of the local problems either developing or becoming worse through an enforced lack of control due to the emergency, the war years appear to have provided the opportunity for many of those in high office in various parts of the tropics to learn of the growing threats of spoliation of vegetation, soil erosion and the wastage of water within their own boundaries.

Obviously the nature, the tempo and the potential dangers of deterioration of vegetation, soil and water vary according to the bioclimatic features.

A rough working impression of the comparative scale of severity is obtainable from the classification in Table XV.

TABLE XV

ROUGH RELATIONSHIP OF POTENTIAL DETERIORATION OF NATURAL VEGETATION, SOIL AND WATER SUPPLY AND THE BIOCLIMATIC REGIONS

Region		Potential deterioration		
		*Vegetation**	*Soil†*	*Water supply‡*
Forest:				
HHF:	highly humid	MS–M–Sl	(S)–MS–M–Sl	M–Sl–N
HF:	humid	(S)–MS–M–Sl	(S)–MS–M–Sl	(MS)–M–Sl
HF–ST:	humid (subtropics)	S–MS–M	S–MS–M	MS–M
HSF:	humid-subhumid	S–MS–(M)	S–MS–M	MS–M
HSF–ST:	humid-subhumid (subtropics)	(VS)–S–MS–M	S–MS–M	(S)–MS–M
HMF:	humid montane	S–MS–M	S–MS–M	S–MS–M
HSMF:	humid-subhumid montane	S–MS–M	S–MS–M	S–MS–M
HMF–ST:	humid montane (subtropics)	S–MS–M	S–MS–M	(VS)–S–MS–M
HSMF–ST:	humid-subhumid montane (subtropics)	(VS)–MS–M	(VS)–MS–M	(VS)–S–MS–M
Edaphic Types in Forest Region:				
PF:	periodically flooded	S–MS–M	S–MS	M–Sl
RF:	riverine and flood plain	S–MS–M	S–MS	M–Sl
FWF:	fresh-water swamp	MS–M–Sl	Not applicable	Not applicable
Wooded Savanna:				
SHWS:	subhumid wooded savanna	(VS)–S–MS	(VS)–S–MS–M	(VS)–S–MS
SHWS–ST:	subhumid wooded (subtropics)	S–MS	S–MS–M	S–MS
SAWS:	subarid wooded savanna	VS–S–MS	(VS)–S–MS–M	VS–S–MS
SAWS–ST:	subarid wooded (subtropics)	(VS)–S–MS	S–MS–M	VS–S–MS
AWS:	arid wooded savanna	VS–S	(VS)–S–MS	VS–S
AWS–ST:	arid wooded (subtropics)	(VS)–S	(VS)–S–MS	VS–S

TABLE XV—*continued*

Region	Potential deterioration		
	Vegetation*	Soil†	Water Supply‡
Subdesert and Desert:			
SD: subdesert	VVS–S–MS	VS–(VS)–S–MS	(VVS)–VS–S
SD–ST: subdesert (subtropics)	VVS–VS–S–MS	VS–(VS)–S–MS	(VVS)–VS
D: desert	VVS–VS–S	(VVS)–VS–S–MS	VVS–VS–S
	(oases, local)	(oases, local)	(oases, local)
D–ST: desert (subtropics)	VVS–VS–S	(VVS)–VS–S–MS	VVS–VS–S
Grassland:			
OG: open grassland:			
montane	S–MS–M	S–MS–M	(VS)–S–MS–M
upland (subtropics)	S–MS–M	S–MS–M	S–MS–M
desert/subdesert grass-land	VVS–VS	(VS)–S–MS	VVS–VS–S
Edaphic Types in Wooded Savanna Subdesert and Grassland:	Much as for the related climatic type, but varies according to clays (less severe) or sandy-loams and sands (more severe)	Clays: less severe, sandy-loams and sands more severe	As for corresponding climatic types, but more severe on clay sites as better storage at depth in sand

VVS: very, very severe
VS: very severe
S: severe
MS: medium-severe
M: moderate
Sl: slight
N: negligible
( ) occasional, not usual
ST: as suffix: subtropics; e.g. SHWS–ST: subhumid wooded savanna (subtropics)
* According to stage and condition of the vegetation, form of cultivation, intensity of grazing or browsing, severity and season of burning and other activities.
† According to soil type, vegetation cover, season, intensity and form of cultivation, crops and cropping method, degree of stocking, season of burning.
‡ According to nature of water—surface, springs, shallow wells, streams, soil type, nature of terrain and of vegetation.

Of its very nature the classification in Table XV is an individual and therefore a subjective one, based on personal observation over a restricted range of country in Latin America and Asia and rather more extensive areas in parts of Africa and to some extent upon the patchy literature. It should be read as a mere indicator only, because the details vary much with precise locality both *bioclimatic* and *edaphic*.

(1) Some Major Causes of Spoliation of Vegetation, Deterioration and Loss of Soils and Loss of Water

I mention briefly some of the more important causes of loss and deterioration in the three natural resources concerned:

(*a*) The consistent destruction of *forest* and other woody growth by axe, fire and in the course of cultivation and pastoral farming has been accomplished over relatively vast areas in the tropics and subtropics.

Probably the reduction in hectarage and the deterioration in quality have been greatest in the humid forests (HF) and in the humid montane forest (HMF), but locally extensive removal and deterioration also have occurred in the highly humid forests (HHF). In the subtropics likewise the forests both humid, at low and medium elevations (HF–ST) and humid montane (HMF–ST) have suffered greatly locally in parts of Latin America, Southern and East Africa and South-East Asia.

Wooded savanna—particularly in its subhumid type (SHWS)—also has been much reduced in quality and area locally and, in parts of Latin America and Africa, over large areas. Here as in the other wooded savanna regions (SAWS: subarid to AWS: arid) the deterioration has taken the form of an accelerated increase in the density of woody growth, especially of tall shrubs and small trees. This intensification and encroachment of woody growth has been discussed in Chapter V and is mentioned again later. In the transition from arid wooded savanna (AWS) to subdesert (SD)—that is in the *ecotone* or transition zone (AWS/SD)—there also is a form of subshrub, shrub and small tree intensification and encroachment of similar ecological nature.

Various other aspects of the deterioration of vegetation are touched upon below.

(b) Of especially great significance in causing the deterioration of vegetation, soils and water supplies is the inefficient land-use so widely practised in the three continents. Its inefficiency springs from its not being based upon rational ecological principles and ordinary common sense.

Clearly the basis for sound land-use is the interplay of the natural vegetation, the local climate and the soils. I do not discount the fact that man, even now, is able to change his environmental pattern fairly profoundly locally, and probably will be able so to do both more intensively and over a much wider range of terrain and conditions in the years ahead. Examples of man's future potential activities are seen in irrigation, drainage, the destruction of forests, the planting of trees, the intensification of scrub and subshrub encroachment and, in the decades to come, through the de-salting of sea and other mineralized waters and its pumping in vast volumes to arid, subdesert and desert areas for both primary and secondary needs.

(*c*) Cultivation—not guided by the most elementary of the principles and practices of soil and water conservation—is a widespread and effective means of deteriorating arable land and of wasting water that well could be conserved in part for various needs. Because of 'shifting cultivation' in the forest and subhumid wooded savannas and the rapid regrowth of natural vegetation on abandoned sites, there is less severe sheet and gully erosion in these bioclimatic regions than in those where the alternation of moist and dry seasons is marked, and where heavy rain plays havoc with soil either bare or only sparsely covered with secondary vegetation.

It is noteworthy that in parts of Latin America, Africa and South-East Asia the indigenous peoples have evolved and handed down to posterity some simple precautionary measures against soil deterioration and erosion. Without attempting an exhaustive list it is instructive to record some of these:

(i) 'Shifting cultivation' itself is the most salutary practice that has been evolved under the prevailing circumstances of : intense radiation; heavy and uniformly distributed rainfall; rain of high intensity irregularly distributed; readily oxidized organic matter, and highly leachable as well as highly erodible soils in the *forests*; and in the *savannas*, soils that often are highly susceptible to sheet and gully erosion when deprived of their vegetative protection.

(ii) In some countries the rural communities have produced simple but often effective devices aimed at reducing run-off and the erosion of soils, especially of those on steep grades. These devices include: strips of grass or other vegetation alternating with strips of cultivation, contour-wise or even slightly graded in relation to the contour plantings, and in places the preparation of simple graded ridges; drainage ditches and remarkably well aligned simple irrigation furrows;* the making of compost either from crop residues and weeds or from a mixture of livestock droppings and vegetable matter; and the utilizing of deeper-rooted short-lived perennials for the rehabilitation of the fertility of arable land cultivated for some seasons—perhaps on the basis of some appreciation of the capacity of these plants to bring to the surface some of the nutrients leached to the lower levels—the so-called 'nutrient cycle' of modern thought.

---

* Remarkable examples of terracing—for rain-fed and irrigable arable alike—are seen in relict and existing forms in various countries in the three continents, particularly in Peru, Ceylon and Malaya.

141

(*Vide* Kellogg and Davol (1949); Phillips (1959B) for references to work by Greenland and Kowal, Nye and others in Africa.)

(*d*) Fire is a bad master when used indiscriminately for such purposes as: the driving of game—from buffalo and antelope to large rodents; the provision of an early but not controlled green bite of grazing and browse for livestock; the destruction of *secondary* vegetation on arable land within the 'shifting cultivation' cycle; and the clearing of primary forest and other vegetation for the initiation of a new cycle of 'shifting cultivation'. Thus employed, fire frequently lays bare vulnerable soil on the less gentle slopes, soil which is washed away by the first subsequent downpour. (*Vide* Cook (1939); Phillips (1930B; 1931; 1936; 1959B) and Bartlett (1956) for further references.) As has been mentioned in Chapter V, fire may be used as an effective means of control, but never should be employed casually and indiscriminately, otherwise the deterioration of grazing and sometimes of browse and the impoverishing and loss of soil inevitably follow.

(*e*) Reference already has been made of the evils of over-grazing and over-browsing and severe trampling of wooded savanna, sub-desert and open grassland, but it is as well to repeat that this common practice in parts of Latin America, Africa and Asia accelerates the deterioration of the quality of the vegetation, the depletion of soil nutrients, the erosion of soil and the wastage of water. In humid montane forest (HMF) and sometimes even in the humid forest (HF) the evil effects of this practice also are evident where severe local over-stocking has been permitted. Signs of deterioration in these humid regions are noticeable in Latin America, Africa and Asia.

(*f*) Linked in some ways with the foregoing is the practice mentioned in Chapter V—the development of water for man and beast in regions where this element is sparse. There is profound danger of inefficient planning and control of the association of man and beast with these additional water sources inducing much harm locally, through the 'trampling out' of vegetation or the intensification of woody growth, the so-called 'bush encroachment'. Where bare ground is the result, the loss of soil and of water of run-off may be severe; where thicket growth is accelerated and accentuated, there is a loss of grazing and browsing and, where there is no ground-cover, a fair measure of run-off down the steeper slopes. It is in the arid to subdesert regions that the risk of this form of deterioration is the greatest (AWS, AWS/SD and SD).

(g) The makers and maintainers of roads and railways in the subhumid to arid to subdesert tropics and subtropics—particularly where the grades are moderate to steep—have accelerated local erosion by ill-designed drainage. Sheet and gully erosion often are very severe where culverts and drains discharge into the adjacent highly erodible terrain, the wounds serving as nuclei for the extension of devastation through over-stocking. Impressive examples of this are frequent in the subarid to arid and subdesert regions in Latin America, Africa and Asia (SAWS, AWS, SD), but are not wanting in the humid ones (HHF, HF, HMF). Several administrations— Peru, South Africa, the Federal Rhodesia, British East Africa, Ghana and Ceylon—are in various stages of study of these particular causes of soil and water loss.

(h) Land tenure has been mentioned elsewhere as one of the causes of deleterious effects of communal grazing, browsing and cultivation upon the soil. Fragmentation, the logical outcome of unsatisfactory tenure, creates conditions conducive to the deterioration of soil and to the loss of water.

(i) An insufficiency of knowledge about certain matters is responsible for serious losses of soil and water and thus for decrease in actual productivity:

(i) Nature and tempo of the wastage of the principal soils in each major bioclimatic subregion, in relation to their characteristics, distribution and responses to various kinds of management.

(ii) Interrelationship of the major climatic factors—such as heat and alternations thereof; humidity and the oscillation thereof; the amount, distribution and intensity of rain; the prevalence and force of the winds and evaporation—and the prevailing forms of deterioration in the soils of a bioclimatic subregion.

(iii) Significance of the natural, semi-natural and variously disturbed vegetation communities as *indicators* of the potentiality for deterioration of the supporting soils, when subjected to precise kinds of pastoral and cultivation practice.

(iv) Influence of specific crops on the physico-chemical and biotic changes in known soils and the economic implications thereof.

(v) Effect of defined practices on the essential characters of specific soils, with reference to:

Selection of the soils and sites for cultivation; provision of appropriate conservation measures; methods and equipment for soil preparation, crop establishment and culture, harvest and post-harvesting treatment of the soil; fertilizing, farmyard manuring, green-manuring and composting of soils and the provision of resting periods—the so-called 'leys'; traditional cultivation practices, such as 'shifting cultivation', more especially were 'sedentary cultivation' to be enforced because of the lack of land for the continuation of 'shifting cultivation'; influence of livestock of various kinds; tree growth—indigenous and exotic—in strategically important sites; and irrigation practice.

In this era of international technical and financial assistance it should not be impossible to assist the administrations, in the countries most needing guidance along the lines mentioned above, in solving their more pressing problems. Funds from outside are less liable to be the restricting influence than is the shortage of really capable, practical as well as scientifically minded investigators and executive officers. Partly this is due to the United States, South Africa, Southern Rhodesia and more, recently in parts, Australia being the only countries in which intensive and extensive experience has been gained in the study and the control of soil and water wastage. Clearly the number of men these countries could spare for assistance programmes would be relatively few. Unfortunately South Africa—one of the best of the potential training grounds—is unlikely to be called upon because of current political tensions.

In the conditions prevailing it would be wise to inaugurate a series of special training courses in the art, science and economics of soil and water conservation in those groups of countries requiring this training. The courses should be at senior and junior level, and should vary in duration, content and emphasis according to the particular problems of the countries participating. It is germane to record that a commendable attempt to organize such a course in late 1962 for 'medium-level' officers in French and English-speaking territories in West Africa is receiving the attention of C.S.A.

In addition to training, however, more attention should be given to the study of some of the scientific and economic issues embraced in this Chapter. The local universities, in collaboration with appropriate academic and other organizations in the highly developed countries, should be encouraged to undertake the investigation of some of the more significant local problems in preventing and in reducing the destruction of natural vegetation, the consequent deterioration and erosion of soil and the wastage of water.

(2) Some Practical Approaches Worthy of Early Attention

Over so diverse a range of conditions existing in the tropics and hotter subtropics it would require several books to set out, in any reasonable measure of detail, the specific needs of each and every country. All that is attempted here is to mention a few of the more pressing needs of a widely recurring kind.

(a) Experience in Southern Rhodesia over the past decade suggests that the 'Intensive Conservation Area' approach promises well for a wide application in some kinds of underdeveloped countries.

Based on a survey of the countrywide conservation and related difficulties, the administration has established a small working committee of local farmers and others for each and every appropriate farming or other district or subdistrict: the 'Intensive Conservation Area'. To this body are attached such local technical conservation staff, senior and junior, as may be appropriate, and to the committee and its technical guides is given the responsibility for the planning, the putting into effect and the financing—according to an agreed schedule of costs and subsidies—of all conservation measures considered to be essential. Tractors and attachments and all relevant supporting materials are held within the district by the technical officers working under the committee. Thus there is less likelihood of time being wasted in the reaching of decisions, the gaining of approval for and the actual accomplishment of conservation works, such as the planning of farms, the protection of arable land against erosion, the building of dams for conservation and other purposes and the rehabilitation of natural pasturage.

It is essential to stress that the responsibility rests upon the local representatives of the farming community and upon those farmers who wish to undertake conservation work upon their own farms, under the auspices of the committee. Furthermore, it is obvious that much depends upon the ability, balance and personality of the technical staff working with the committee. Because of these two important features it is manifest that the application of the approach is restricted to those countries and those localities within a country where the farming community is progressive, intelligent, imaginative and willing to help itself, and where technical personnel is present in sufficiency at a requisite standard of ability and experience. Unfortunately, therefore, the direct application of this approach could be made only in a still comparatively small proportion of countries in the tropics and hotter subtropics.*

But there is no reason why some suitable local modification of the approach should not be tried in any country where the farmers are beset by conservation problems, are anxious to see something done about the solving of these and are willing to co-operate, in their own way, so as to make these solutions possible in practice. The providing of suitable technical personnel would not be easy, especially in the initial stages, but by dint of careful selection, the arranging for special training and for periodic checking and refreshing of the personnel, some progress should be possible within a decade. It is important that a beginning should be made—through a few reliable local farmers and technical staff. Success breeds success, hence it is imperative that the initial attempts should not fail but be successful.

(b) In countries where the overwhelming majority of the cultivators and pastoralists are simple people, more often than not either wholly or largely illiterate, an approach that is promising some success in Basutoland is worthy of consideration: the promulgation and the steady rehabilitation of a 'conservation area' or whatever else it might be termed most aptly locally. Within this area, chosen for some specific reason such as it being the deteriorating territory of a particular tribe or community, the principle of approach is to win the interest, the mind, the heart and the hands of the local leaders, their advisers and sooth-sayers and their cultivators and the pastoralists. However sound the technical approaches may be as to both the *mechanical* (or engineering) aspects and the *biological* or (crop production and livestock husbandry) ones, the full success feasible under the local circumstances will not be attained unless the *psychological* victory be won. The spirit of the people must be evoked. With this all things are possible, within reason, but without this, the administration—even a national one—will expend time, energy, money and much patience in striving *to do for the people* what they

---

* An attempt to establish intensive conservation area committees in Native Purchase Areas (wherein Africans have an individual tenure) is being made in Southern Rhodesia: 1961. This imaginative approach should provide information of great interest.

should want *to do for themselves*. (*Vide* Phillips (1960B) regarding the fine work in Basutoland, which could have achieved so much more had the Africans been led to do more for themselves.)

Approaches of the kind mentioned below are applicable, *mutatis mutandis* among many peoples in the tropics and hotter subtropics. These involve winning the co-operation of the people for the re-planning of pastoral areas, arable lands and residential sites; for the application of methods and practices of agricultural and engineering nature for the conservation of desirable vegetation and of soil and water; and for the general raising of their economy and standards of living.

(*c*) When 'shifting cultivation' perforce is nearing an end—because of a rapid increment in an already large population for the dimensions and resources of the particular locality and because the area available for cultivation is limited—an urgent demand arises for each and every device and practice for maintaining the fertility and the physical and biotic well-being of the soil to be farmed *nolens volens* in the future on the 'sedentary' basis. 'Sedentary cultivation' naturally makes heavy demands upon the soil and also upon the ingenuity of the cultivator. Gone are the halcyon years of moving from one patch of land to another and leaving Nature to refurbish, on the temporarily abandoned patch, the nutrients depleted by cropping without the aid of additional nutriment in the form of fertilizer or manure.

It remains to be proven whether the following will maintain the soil in good heart: the balanced use of chemical fertilizers and locally available animal or plant organic matter; a rotation of crops bringing in proven nutrifiers such as known legumes and especially those of deeper rooting habit; an approach to 'mixed' arable and livestock farming; and the use of improved varieties of hardy and resistant crops by observant and industrious cultivators.

In this challenging task the cultivator needs all the practical and scientific guidance available—but that is not readily come by in the form of men who have gained long local experience, and who, at the same time, possess or could gain in time the confidence of the communities. Technical assistance certainly should not, like the proverbial gift horse, be 'looked in the mouth', but in the nature of the task awaiting him the average technical assistance officer from abroad has much to learn before he himself can be of much prac-tical significance locally. We must begin, otherwise there never will be a sufficiency of technical assistance adequately informed as to the local patterns, problems and possibilities: but let the beginning be based soundly on reliable advisers.

(*d*) Although manifestly an approach essential to true progress in the control of floods and consequent erosion if not devastation, the protection of water-sheds large, medium and small, hitherto has not received the practical attention it demands. Unquestionably costly in really great catchments and not cheap even in medium ones, the protection of the small water-sheds lies within the resources of most governments, provided they call in the moral and the practical co-operation of the local rural communities. Until funds are available for the conservation of the large and the medium water-sheds, these small ones should be treated as required. This normally could be in the form of protection of the vegetation, on strategically important sites, from destruction by cultivators, fire and livestock; and the allocation of residential, arable and pastoral areas so that these do not threaten the sources of supply of water and the often readily erodible steeper slopes and drainage lines.

Simple and restricted as these contributions to the protection of the small water-sheds might appear to be, the resultant benefits cannot be gainsaid. Were protection to be extended to the vast number of petty water-sheds in Latin America, Africa and Asia, much water and soil would be prevented from slipping away with the floods and to the sea.

(*e*) Water development for man, beast and irrigation obviously could be on a grand scale—as seen in some of the great man-made 'lakes' in all the continents concerned—or by means of a large number of appropriately placed small dams, simple wells and ably chosen bore-holes. Both of these approaches will be made increasingly, especially in the subhumid to the subdesert and desert regions. It is to the provision of the simple means of conservation and the supplying of water that I more especially wish to direct attention —because by these the local supplies could be augmented and new sites provided with water to a reasonable extent in the course of a decade.

Elsewhere I have endeavoured to stress the dangers of providing additional or new water supplies where hitherto the amounts available have been sparse and far dispersed. Here again I emphasize that it often might be wiser, in the *ultimate* interests of man, beast, soil and vegetation to provide no additional or new waters, rather than to create these in a casual pattern and to fail to regulate the numbers of livestock dependent thereon. Undoubtedly this simple ecological fact will be the cause of much argument, but, if not accepted in practice, will damn the otherwise good and generous efforts of American and other technical aid. (*Vide* Phillips (1956) and (1960B) *re* Somalia and Bechuanaland respectively, in this respect.)

As the correct distribution and control of additional and new water supplies in the subhumid to the desert regions (SHWS, SAWS, AWS, SD) directly affects the conservation of the vegetation, the soil and of water from rainfall, I re-emphasize this matter at this point.

(*f*) At first sight the suggestion that conservation of vegetation, soil and water could be aided in the tropics and hotter subtropics by means of efficient planning of farm land might seem far fetched, because of the vast and widespread preponderance of 'shifting cultivation', of small patches of 'sedentary cultivation' and of communal grazing and browse. On estates and larger farms, of course, the principle of planning these so as to make the best use of the features of the vegetation, physiography and soils obviously is sound. Records of the good results following the rational land use planning in North America, in Southern Rhodesia and in South Africa, for example, fully justify this approach wherever feasible.

But the systematic planning of 'shifting cultivation' and of its ultimate successor, 'sedentary cultivation' is by no means impossible. But certainly this will be difficult because it demands not only special technical knowledge of local cropping, productivity of soil and of conservation but also of the traditional psychology of the local cultivators. When their customs and practices merely are examined, let alone the subject of potential modification even at the hands of a trusted national government, these simple people may react strongly against proposed changes in their ways of production.

As nationals of the various countries more and more join the public services—especially in the legal, agricultural, community development and other relevant branches—it might become possible for local if not wider regional planning of cultivated and pastoral land to be put into practice. This is being done, with promising indications so far, in local conservation areas in Basutoland, in parts of Kenya and elsewhere in Africa. But the co-operation of the local community must be gained from the outset, otherwise no certain progress could be made by a regiment of surveyors, soils men, agronomists and conservationists, no matter what their race or creed.

(g) From all this it is evident that education, community development, demonstration, technical guidance and leadership as well as money are essential for the reclaiming of what has been disturbed and for the conserving of what is still intact in the vegetation, soils and waters of the tropics and hotter subtropics.

Legislation too has its part to play, but probably in special instances only: such as the promulgation of certain catchments or other areas as 'conservation districts', for the sound planning of community water supplies, wise usage of riparian water, and the prevention of spoliation of the natural resources therein. Emphatically a suitable *code of water laws* must be linked with such promulgation before the development and perhaps spoliation of riparian and other waters have gone too far.

(II) The Biotic Balance

By *biotic balance* is implied the ecological relationships binding the community of plants, animals and man—the *biotic* community —with its environment, throughout the development of both. A community in the course of growth and development is in equilibrium or balance with the environment at each and every phase, from the pioneer to the final or *climax*. As this balance is for ever changing in greater or less detail, it has been termed *dynamic* balance or equilibrium. References to the concept and literature may be found in the contributions by Clements (1916), Phillips (1930A; 1934; 1935A and B; 1949; 1959B), Clements and Shelford (1939) and Fraser Darling (1956). As mentioned in Chapter III, the concept has been criticized in W. L. Thomas *et al.* (1956) by several sociological economists who believe that ecologists have paid insufficient attention to *disequilibrium* because of their alleged obsession with *equilibrium*. As an understanding of the *biotic balance* has a direct bearing upon all aspects of agriculture and forestry—the conservation and management of soil, water, wild life and vegetation; the control of pests, diseases and vermin; and the living and the movements of man and his animals—I touch upon the concept and give several examples of its application in the tropics and subtropics.

An impressive example of the intimate interplay of the following phenomena exists in the biology, ecology and bionomics of the Tsetse (*Glossina* spp.): (1) the various climatic and soil factors and the seasonal changes thereof; (2) plant communities seasonally and at different stages in their successional development; (3) the behaviour of wild animals great and small according to season; (4) trypanosomes capable of inducing partial resistance, disease and death in man and domesticated animals; and (5) a vector varying strikingly in its responses to the factors of light, heat, humidity and evaporation as conditioned by the plant communities. (*Vide* Swynnerton (1936) for references; Phillips (1930c; 1932; 1949; 1956; 1959b).)

Confined to ecologically appropriate but very extensive portions of Trans-Saharan tropical Africa, Tsetse—as the vector of animal and human trypanosomiasis (*Nagana* and Sleeping-sickness respectively)—definitely exerts two far-reaching influences: *firstly*, it retards the expansion and the general well-being of man, livestock production and cultivation and, *secondly*, it serves as a protector of vegetation, water and soils from spoliation where man makes no provision for the conservation of these natural resourses.

Suitably applied and maintained alterations in the *biotic balance* —such as in the selective thinning of vegetation so as to increase the light intensity and temperature under its canopy, or the destruction or other means of control of wild animals serving as blood reservoirs and therefore as sources of trypanosomes—indeed would reduce the fly or cause it to disappear. But this *imbalance* or *disequilibrium* must be maintained consistently, otherwise Nature again would adjust the balance and back would come the fly. But it is just here that man either may convert the *temporary* state of imbalance to one of *modified* balance or may introduce circumstances that inevitably result in a serious and *permanent* imbalance. On the one hand he may manage the areas cleared of Tsetse so as to conserve or improve the vegetation cover, the water supplies and the soils, and at the same time obtain reasonable returns from livestock or arable farming. On the other, by permitting an excessive multiplication of livestock, he may induce the evil effects of over-grazing and over-browsing and may ruin arable land by feckless crop and soil husbandry. Unfortunately it is the second that almost invariably happens, simply because hitherto no government has had the wisdom and the courage to ensure that the first is achieved. The national governments now have an opportunity of proving that they possess a vision and a courage that no Colonial administration ever has demonstrated in this regard.*

* It is scarcely necessary to note that lack of co-operation and self-help on the part of Africans often has been the basic problem facing the colonial powers. It is doubtful whether African administrations will find their own nationals much different in these respects.

CONSERVATION OF SOIL, WATER

An example from arid Africa (AWS, AWS/SD and SD) illustrates another aspect of the delicacy of the *biotic balance* and the risks attached to approaches tending to its disturbance: the recently expressed desire of some organizations to 'settle' the nomadic and the transhumant peoples. Fraser Darling (1956; 1957)* has warned against the facile assumption that the carrying of livestock *permanently* on restricted areas within the subregions in which nomadic and transhumant peoples and their livestock migrate is a happy sociological and economic solution. I myself believe that its true success is rare and special. Of Somalia I certainly believe (Phillips, 1957) that to change the way of life of these migrants would cause trouble. Not only are these peoples not easily persuaded to settle, but were they to do so on even a moderate scale, the destruction of vegetation and soil and the consequent loss of vigour and of life in livestock would be disastrous.

What would happen to any particular terrain and its people were nomads to be 'settled' in the absence of careful planning and preparation for their winning of a living and maintaining the productivity of their environment, is only a special example of a more general form of imbalance—widespread in the subarid to subdesert regions (SAWS, AWS/SD, SD)—due to uncontrolled grazing and browsing of the indigenous vegetation. As already mentioned originally fairly valuable pasturage and browse can be converted by selective feeding to either a much less palatable grassland or to an almost impenetrable thicket of thorny and other woody subshrubs, shrubs and trees. In other communities, according to the circumstances, bare ground is increased at the expense of the vegetative cover, with consequent sheet and gully erosion. In the transition zones—between arid and subdesert and subdesert and desert subregions (AWS, SD, SD/D)—the imbalance caused by over-stocking encourages the advance of the more arid or xerophytic vegetation. Examples of this are found in some of the drier localities in Latin America, but much more dramatically and on a grander scale in arid to subdesert Africa and in equivalent sectors in Asia. Unless timely precautions be taken the more xerophytic vegetation will advance on a vast scale in vulnerable soils of Latin America, Africa and Asia.

Enough has been said about the delicacy of balance between well-organized 'shifting cultivation' and the conservation of the soils of

* *Vide* also Pearsall (1957), Twining (1958) and Thomas (1960) on beast and man in the Serengeti, Tanganyika.

the forest and the wooded savanna, to indicate the dangers inherent in its enthusiastic attempted substitution by 'sedentary' settlement But very much more should be known about the farming and the conserving of land *permanently* settled before a general change could be advocated. What is now in *temporary* imbalance, but very soon could strike a new balance between man and soil, could become very rapidly a serious *permanent* imbalance: the deterioration of soil and the consequent impoverishment of crops and those endeavouring to produce them.

The interest being shown in parts of Latin America, Africa and Asia in intensifying cultivation and livestock farming in the forest regions (HHF, HF and HMF) is producing the first signs of a local imbalance: the sensitive forest soils are being depleted of their evanescent nutriment and are being sheet eroded and gullied. Attempts to clear fairly large areas for cultivation and livestock husbandry are raising many problems, due to the imbalance in the ecological relations of the local biotic communities and soils. It is certain that attempts at intensive and extensive colonization in the forest regions during the coming decade will provide many examples of serious imbalance. This threat is particularly strong in the *selva* of South America, in West Africa and the former Belgian Congo, in Burma, Ceylon, Malaya, Indonesia and probably elsewhere in Asia.

Because of the awakening of interest in Nature conservancy—national parks, game reserves and the like—in the tropics and subtropics, the threat of a widely spread imbalance from the unimaginative *over-protection* of wild animals also is increasing. Attention has been drawn to this danger in North America and Africa, more especially, and consequently to the urgent need for introducing wild life management of a progressive kind to all Nature reserves. Among the foremost students of this subject is Fraser Darling, whose observations in Scotland, parts of North America and several sectors in Africa deserve study. In several large 'game reserves' in Southern and Eastern Africa strong evidence exists of the detrimental influences upon both vegetation and wild animals of a casual protection policy, inevitably producing an imbalance among the various species of wild life and the vegetation and therefore also the wild life, the vegetation and the soil.

The protection of delicately balanced vegetation and soil conditions—as in some parts of the more severe subdeserts of the Kalahari, Angola, the northerly portions of West and Equatorial Africa,

Kenya, parts of the Sudan, Ethiopia and the Somali Republic—in the interests of both man and wild animals of many kinds is a task to which must be drawn the serious attention of the territorial administrations, U.N.E.S.C.O. and I.U.C.N. (International Union for Conservation of Nature and Natural Resources). By effective control and management it should be possible to conserve and simultaneously make a small contribution toward the costs of management. To throw these delicately balanced areas open for feckless livestock production of the common pattern would spell their earlier deterioration and, in parts, early destruction.*†

I have suggested elsewhere the possibility of this atomic age seeing the irrigation of extensive areas hitherto considered beyond the reach of a sufficiency of water. Not discounting the many valuable results of intensive and extensive irrigation in the arid to desert regions (AWS, AWS/SD, SD/D, D), it should be remembered that several kinds of *imbalance* could occur. Among these could be the development of alkali (brack) conditions in some soil types; the leaching of nutrients from soils moderately rich in these because of the prevailing dryness of the climate; and the washing and erosion of the soils wherever the cultivator is ignorant of the principles and practice of conservation. The edaphic changes will be reflected fairly early in impoverished production.

Many other examples exist but enough has been said to indicate the ease with which *biotic balance* is convertible to *imbalance* or *disequilibrium*. A plea is made, therefore, to the appropriate administrations and international bodies to investigate objectively the features of vital importance in the principal *biotic communities* in the main bioclimatic regions, in order that their *biotic balance* may be better understood before large-scaled development of any kind be attempted.

* A particularly important example of delicate biotic equilibrium exists in part of the Kalahari, worthy of early investigation. (*Vide* Phillips (1960B).)

† At the meeting of I.U.C.N. in Warsaw, June 1960, it was agreed that I.U.C.N., F.A.O., U.N.E.S.C.O. and C.C.T.A./C.S.A. should study the problems of conservation of *fauna, flora* and *soil* in Africa. A preparatory committee was appointed to draw up a statement for the consideration of the various governments in the *tropics* of the continent in the first instance. This is a commendable first step, due largely to the initiative of Messrs. Th. Monod, Fraser Darling and Worthington. The economics of conservation are included in the programme of study. Several American investigators commenced a study of wild life management in Southern Rhodesia in 1960.

CHAPTER VIII

Some Highly Important Facilities and Services

Assuming that within a country or a district thereof it is feasible to produce materials for subsistence and exchange it then remains to ensure that the best possible usage is made of these. This implies the arrangement of conditions and facilities usually still either wholly lacking or poorly provided in many tropical and hotter subtropical countries. These are storage both near the point of production and at some depot, processing—more often at some depot but occasionally at the producing point—communications, marketing and co-operative movements. Each of these topics could justify a chapter to itself but here I can do no more than mention them briefly.

Storage

In many countries the storage of products at the points of origin is either lacking or, at best, is poor. But in some of the more developed districts of some countries the progressive farmers have built really up-to-date stores and silos and provide effective means of controlling vermin, insects, fungi and other destructive agents. The larger countries in Latin America, the West Indies, South Africa, Southern Rhodesia, parts of East Africa and some parts of India provide examples of this.

For the small producer—usually the indigenous or naturalized cultivator and pastoralist—the facilities steadily have been improved during the past ten years—notably in some of the Latin American and West Indian countries; South Africa, the Federation of Rhodesia and Nyasaland, Tanganyika, Kenya, parts of Nigeria, and districts in the former Belgian Congo, one-time French territories in West Africa, Angola and Moçambique; and parts of Pakistan, India, Ceylon and Malaya. But in all of these still much remains to be done to make the conditions satisfactory for a substantial proportion of the rural communities.

It is to the credit of some of the simple cultivators in the three continents that they have evolved gradually in the course of time their own primitive but occasionally fairly effective means of storage of grain and legumes—various patterns of pit silo being chosen with forethought as to topography and type of soil within easy reach. Indeed so good are some of these that it is not necessary to do more than improve their design and structure and to provide for the control of vermin, insects, fungi and other agents of deterioration. But here again, much more could be done to make these basically satisfactory and cheap stores more effective against dampness or excessive dryness and the depredations of organisms.

Fortunately the F.A.O. and the territorial administrations alike are showing a steadily growing interest in improving local methods of storage and in introducing modern ideas. World Bank Missions frequently have advocated the giving of special attention to the improvement of the facilities for storage, both at the points of production and at the urban or port bases. Local and other funds scarcely could be used to better advantage.

Processing

Here the emphasis is not upon the processing—usually reasonably to even highly efficient—of standard commodities such as sugar, tea, coffee, meat, copra, various oils, fibres, rubber and major forest products by progressive private or quasi-government enterprise, but upon the relatively simple processing of certain products by small cultivators and pastoralists in the rural areas.

The many kinds of products so often wastefully prepared include milk, cream, ghee, cheese, buffalo-curd; dried meat and fish; hides, skins, mohair and wool (subtropics) and bone meal, honey, dried banana and plantain; papein, sundry millets and sorghums, maize, rice and legumes; potato products (South America), cassava (*Manihot*), yams (*Dioscorea*); copra and oils; fibres, including local and exotic kinds; various local alcohols; resins, barks and hand-sawn timber.

Varying with country, district, community and individual producer, these and various other commodities frequently are poorly prepared for storage and transport. In far-flung communities, isolated because of very poor roads, the wastage in the simple preparation or home processing of the more readily perishable products is moderate to very high. In recent years the stimulus given by demonstrations and advice by F.A.O. and by some of the local administrations has begun to produce a salutary response, but what I have said of the scope for improvement in storage applies equally well here.

More and more support should be given to those administrations and communities showing willingness to co-operate in a practical manner with those capable of assisting in raising the standards of the small producers. This need for improved local processing frequently has drawn the attention of World Bank Missions.

Communications

Almost without exception the lines of communication in tropical and the hotter subtropical countries are either meagre to poor or are developed locally only. In light of their previous comparative isolation this is to be understood, but now that world policy is to assist in the rapid development of these regions, and particularly their rural communities, more thought is being given to the possibilities of rendering the farther reaches more accessible.

World Bank loans and advice as well as support from other external sources have been directed to the improvement of trunk roads, railways, river navigation, ports—river and marine, airports, telecommunications and the like.

It should be said of roads that although an encouraging amount of attention is being given to the establishment and maintenance of trunk and secondary roads, the minor or 'feeder' ones for the extraction of products from the farms to the larger roads still are too few, ill distributed, mal-aligned and commonly very poorly maintained, especially during the wet seasons. It is the experience of all who have shown interest in these subsidiary links that the substantial increase and improved maintenance have played a helpful part in stimulating agricultural activity in districts which previously were unable to send to the larger roads and the railways any of the heavier products of either subsistence or exchange kind. I myself have noted this particularly in such diverse African countries as South Africa, Tanganyika, Somalia and Ghana and am impressed with what I have been told of the good results following similar developments in parts of Latin America and Asia. Satisfactory maintenance of 'feeder' roads made by the administration, by communal or other local enterprise or by a combination of state and local funds and labour, however, still is a difficulty because of poverty of funds, equipment and supervision. A common *pattern* and *problem*, these demand more sympathetic and practical attention before the full *promise* of this kind of road can be fulfilled. International aid well might be directed toward the working out of appropriate local solutions for this common difficulty.

In regions of grand physiographic character—as in much of South America where the mighty Andes are especially challenging to the engineer and the economist, in certain parts of Africa and of Asia —the immense and repeatedly varying alterations in elevation imply vast expenditure upon trunk and other roads for motorized transport. However heavy this might be, in the long view this expenditure from national sources—augmented by loans from within and from beyond the countries concerned—should be faced, if there is a reasonable chance that the resulting development of the agricultural, forestry and other natural resources later will justify the cost. A striking example is seen in Peru, where timber and sundry commodity and subsistence products find their way to the outer world only by means of a tortuous river and ocean journey, whereas good trunk roads across the Andes not only could assist local industry on the Pacific coast but render much shorter ocean transport to the United States.*

Because of the amazing improvement in the efficiency of road transport, and the steady gain in weight and volume of transport by means of aeroplanes, the scope for *railway* expansion in the remoter portions of the tropics and subtropics is less certain today than it appeared to be many years ago. The great expense of railway development also is a factor to be remembered.

Railway engineering faces especially complex problems in the great mountains, escarpments, valleys and rivers so frequently encountered in some of the tropical and subtropical countries.

On the *economic* side the traversing of often great expanses of low-yielding arid to desert country (SAWS, AWS, AWS/SD, SD, SD/D and D regions) commonly offering poor pay-loads, if no mining areas exist, quite often is an obstacle to railway expansion. Examples of these circumstances are found in the more arid sectors of Africa and Asia. Railways of this kind also have been inherited in some countries—because of an earlier considered strategic value they possessed. Railways laid for purely temporary political reasons also are not unknown in Latin America, parts of Africa and in some Asian countries. Definitely the potential economy of the country traversed never could have justified their establishment.

* A World Bank loan of $ U.S. 5·5 million for improvement of road transport between the Amazon in eastern Peru and Lima thus is apt: Dec. 1960.

It cannot be emphasized sufficiently that current and future costs, the competition from roads and the air and the doubtful economics of much of the land to be traversed should be weighed by the international and other authorities responsible for advising territorial administrations not only about the expansion of railways but also about the retention of lines of little if any apparent *promise.*

Communications have been excellent from time immemorial on some of the great rivers in Latin America and to a lesser but still impressive extent in portions of West Africa, the former Belgian Congo and Asia. Doubtless there is scope for an improvement of these—better and more efficiently equipped craft and river ports, the cutting of linking canals where tortuous bends incur lengthy travel that could be reduced at a cost, and the design of craft more suitable for river transport. Very occasionally a grandiose proposal for river development finds its way to international and other authorities for consideration in relation to an application for loans, but fortunately these very rarely are blessed by the referees!

Doubtless the future will see a much greater use of both passenger and freight aeroplanes in the still hidden reaches of many tropical and hotter subtropical lands. Livestock, meat, vegetables and various other comparatively lucrative commodities definitely will be airborne during the next twenty-five years: the day of the giant freighter is still to come. A heavy expenditure upon 'feeder' air services and 'bush' or 'desert' landing grounds must be faced in the interests of local rural, mining and other development. International technical assistance and financial aid increasingly should be directed toward this new development.

It is feasible that the recently designed 'cushioncraft' intended to transport bananas over bad roads and seasonably unnavigable rivers in West Africa (Elder and Fyffe are to test one of these in the Cameroons) might be developed for other transport purposes. The roads over which the craft is to 'skim', at 12 to 15 inches height above ground, would demand good maintenance and, in the drier regions and seasons, protection against wind erosion from air blast around the bottom edge of the craft.*

Among the most frustrating of experiences in the routine of

* Jan. 1961: Five British firms are building this type of 'Hovercraft' or 'Cushioncraft' capable of ferrying weights of 4 to 25 tons at speeds up to 30 to 80 miles per hour, and designed to transport agricultural products, vehicles and passengers for road and river service in Africa and elsewhere.

business in many of the tropical and subtropical countries, far removed from the developed world, are the absence or the comparatively sparseness of *telecommunications* and the inefficiency in their maintenance and working. Naturally this general weakness goes to swell the volume of the obstacles in the way of progressive agricultural and related development, and for this reason, should be removed with the support of international and other external resources. It is true, of course, that compared with forty and even thirty years ago the current distribution and efficiency of posts and telegraphs are very much better than they were. It was safer to send a 'telegram' by relay runners than by official telegraph in some parts of East Africa in the 'twenties, and in some countries in the same continent it to this day is wiser to rely upon a mailed confirmation of a telegram or cable than upon the signalled message itself.

Marketing

Varying in degree with the country, the local marketing of food and other domestic needs often is a vexed matter. By contrast the well-ordered marketing organizations dealing with major internationally required commodities like sugar, tea, coffee, cocoa, banana, hides and skins, cotton, sisal, copra, rubber and timber normally run smoothly so long as they do not suffer interference for political reasons.

Food and other local requisites rarely are disposed of at local and even at urban markets in other than a casual and chancy manner. But this of course varies with country—in parts of Latin America, West Africa and Asia the local traders, men and sometimes women, act as either individuals or group marketing agents and with remarkable facility and ingenuity. These may be, but often are not, grouped with middle-men and speculators who make lucrative 'killings'. In some countries the co-operative movements help to organize the local marketing, particularly of selected products but in many others they play little if any effective part in this.

Where abattoirs and meat canneries exist in the three continents the marketing of livestock normally is arranged to ensure an incentive and therefore a reasonable continuity in the supply of animals for slaughter or export on hoof.

Attempts are being exerted by the F.A.O. and other organizations to improve markets and marketing procedure in some of the tropical and subtropical countries, and this well-intentioned but refractory work deserves all possible support. From contacts with the marketing problems in various countries I conclude that no permanent improvement should be expected until there is a much higher proportion of the indigenous or other local people—of proven ability and integrity—prepared to devote themselves to the planning and the maintenance of sound marketing. Buildings and regulations are essential to satisfactory business, but unless these be in the charge of men and women of more than ordinary reliability they cannot make the difference between the casual and even disorderly and irregular practices that at present pass for marketing and efficiency.

I do not attempt to discuss the involved topic of the marketing boards of the kind created for specific commodities—such as cocoa, coffee, tobacco and some other commodities during the last war in some British and other colonial territories—because of the perhaps inevitable local politics involved in their existence and practices. These played a significant and helpful rôle from the angles both of the producers and the local governments, during and after the war. Their alleged disadvantages have been aired by some economists and politicians, but until something more generally satisfactory is acceptable to the authorities it would be wrong to liquidate these boards. From specific levies well husbanded it has been possible for some administration to finance important development directly and otherwise related to the particular commodity, and even to support other national undertakings sometimes only remotely linked with agriculture in its widest sense.

Agricultural Co-operatives

The co-operative movement—usually working according to the standard patterns—does exist in many of the tropical and subtropical countries and of course varies greatly in its scope, organization, efficiency and influence according to the country and the kind of co-operative. Although notable progress toward self-help has been made in some countries and in others in the development of particular agricultural interests, it still is too often true that the movement is ineffectual and depends too much upon either official or foreign leadership. Stimulus from above remains commoner than inspiration from within. Although established very late, the co-operatives in

11   161

African rural areas in Southern Rhodesia are impressive because of their being well run *from within*.

Clearly there is scope for the infusion of more purpose and vitality into a large proportion of the co-operatives and for the establishment of others, provided these are soundly based and self-stimulating after the initial assistance given them. The F.A.O. and other interested organizations are endeavouring to aid the local administrations in the clearing of difficulties facing the movement. As in so many other vital activities upon which a more progressive agriculture and the marketing of its products must depend, the principal need of the co-operative movement is a sufficiency of nationals of the requisite standards of reliability and ability. Foreign advisers and executives for a time are able to assist the development of the movement, but in the long run its efficiency and integrity, whether for purchasing and sale of products or for the husbanding of and the distribution of funds for loans, must be decided by the quality of the local official personnel and by the members and their representatives. In this way alone will an 'inner vitality' be born within the movement.

Labour in Agriculture

At the risk of inciting the criticism of I.L.O. and other interests directly concerned with labour in the various senses in which this is associated with agriculture in the tropics and subtropics, I feel impelled to comment on several matters of pervading importance.

Doubtless much of the indigenous or naturalized labour, privately engaged or however otherwise recruited, in these regions is inefficient by the accepted Western standards of possible achievement of particular tasks per man-day of ten or twelve hours. Among the reasons for this perhaps the more weighty are: (1) The background of tradition that dictates that man, woman or child should not work for more than a proportion of a day, a month, a season or a year; (2) the often somewhat lower standards of health, reserve of stamina and initiative compared with those in the cooler subtropics and the temperate region; (3) the still too sparse existence of employers, managers, foremen, instructors and demonstrators capable of setting suitably pitched standards of technical, semi-technical and ordinary industriousness and pride in the particular form of agricultural enterprise in which the labour is employed; (4) the failure of government and private enterprise to furnish a sufficiently high proportion of executive staff, senior and junior, blessed with the gifts of understanding and of sympathetic leadership; (5) the want of an attractive nature of incentive for the stimulation of a sincere and consistent desire on the part of labour to continue and to improve in its service —by contrast with the example set by some of the mining organizations in the three continents the efforts exerted by so many of the larger employers of agricultural labour are poor, but notable exceptions there are of course from Latin America to South-East Asia; (6) the occasionally great distances from which labour is recruited —sometimes from countries some thousands of miles distant—and the often appreciable period of service for which it is engaged; six to twenty-four months at a stretch.

Because of these and probably other local reasons the indigenous or naturalized labour often justifiably can be classified as *expensive* —its output is comparatively slight despite its apparently low rate of pay and the simple accommodation and perquisites granted. As said previously (Phillips, 1959B: 325), I believe that this is explicable on ecological grounds. Peoples unaccustomed to long and consistent labour, living in warmth and high humidity or in very hot and arid climates, not used to systematic exertion and having the simplest needs and few aspirations, cannot be expected to dedicate themselves during a term of service nor even during a generation to the standards of their foreign or national employers. When in addition to these normal inherited traits they suffer from pests, diseases and ill housing and feeding, and are set low standards of example by their employers, the reasons for their lack of interest, initiative and drive readily are explicable.

I have had some contact with labourers at various times in Africa and have compared with these, in a general manner, the responses of men in other parts of the tropics. I firmly believe that through demonstration, example and leadership at foreman and all other levels, an improvement in health and in working conditions and, where labour is resident, in living conditions, and the introduction of task or piece-work incentive, where feasible, much could be done to stimulate the interest and the responsibility of the indigenous workers. Once again I appeal for the winning of the heart and mind of man even as I stress the necessity for caring for his physical needs. The gainful employment of men, women and children in the agriculture and forestry of the tropics and subtropics would establish their significant intrinsic value, and lead to their greater happiness and enhanced political stability.

CHAPTER IX

The Aiding of Agricultural and Related Development and General Conclusions

Background

One of the happier outcomes of the last war has been the acceptance—apparently sincere if not wholly altruistic as indeed it would be difficult to be because of human cupidity—that the underdeveloped countries of the world should be helped toward a fuller life by those which are either highly or semi-developed. The United Nations Organization and its various agencies, ranging from the specialist ones such as F.A.O. and W.H.O. to the unique International Bank for Reconstruction and Development, have dedicated thought and funds to the improvement of the lot of man in those countries less privileged. Compared with the days before the war the attention shown and the helpful services provided the underdeveloped world are indeed remarkable.

Of the underdeveloped countries a high proportion occurs in the tropics and the hotter subtropics.

Although it would be incorrect to generalize that the temperate and the cooler subtropical regions ever and always provide less difficult settings for man and his welfare—and notably for his agriculture and forestry—the very poverty of scientific and other systematically collected information about the tropics and the hotter subtropics makes infinitely more complex the task of assisting these regions toward happier circumstances.

From what is known of these circumstances—and the foregoing chapters are a mere summary of some of the challenges inherent therein—it is obvious that climate, soils, vegetation, fauna, human health and comfort, culture, sociology and religion, education and training, imports and exports and last, but not least, economics and finance—all in their own ways and interrelations weave a tapestry of great intricacy.

164

Closely interwoven with this are the all-pervading way of life, agriculture and, in the humid tropics and subtropics, the potentially ubiquitous if not eternal forest and all that it offers for and against human happiness. The satisfactory development of these great industries and ways of life presents features both difficult and encouraging—and my object is to direct attention to some of more than ordinary significance to all who wish to aid that development.

Certain Features of Prime Significance in the Satisfactory Development of Agriculture and Forestry

(1) From what I have seen, heard and read of the broad subject of the tropics and the hotter subtropics I believe that the race between the increase in population and the production of a sufficiency of food and related organic materials could be won by the art, science and discipline of crop and livestock production—but only if some basic provisos be met. These include:

(a) A really effective means of *birth control* acceptable by peoples of multifarious traditions and religions in the tropics and subtropics must be found. At present the means are not effective and the overwhelming mass of public opinion—even could this be deemed such and gathered without arousing suspicions and antagonisms—would be against the acceptance of any means of contraception.*

(b) Truly progressive agricultural policies and practices must be evolved and applied within the major potentially productive countries. These policies and practices—to be sound—must embrace all aspects of the production of crops and livestock, their welfare, the storage and the processing of their yields, a wholly satisfactory conservation if not amelioration of the prime resources of soil and a balanced supply of water.

(c) Sufficient water of the requisite quality—that is not strongly mineralized and thus potentially harmful to man, livestock, fish and soil—must be available for all the purposes of agriculture—especially drinking, irrigation, associated industries and freshwater fisheries.

This certainly would involve the de-mineralizing or 'de-salting'

---

* It is said by some that birth control is less urgent in these regions than often is stressed and that the West has harmed its own position relative to the Soviet and the East by over-control of population. While agreeing with the second view I cannot support the first.

of marine and saline inland waters and probably the pumping of these conditioned resources to localities where suitable irrigable land exists in appropriate pattern and dimensions (*vide* Cockcroft (1955), Moyers (1957) and Jenkins (1960)). Vast returns of annual food crops and large ones of commodity perennials yielding cocoa, coffee, edible oils, copra and the like could be ensured by research, project undertakings, advice, guidance, good organization and management. Great herds and flocks of livestock could be based upon these irrigation settlements and ranches, providing dairy and other products as required. Wise animal and pastoral husbandry, supported by veterinary measures, alone could ensure as full a success as possible in propositions of the kind implied, but even the small pastoralist suitably guided could make an effective contribution to the return of livestock and their products.

Portions of the subarid to desert regions (SAWS, AWS, AWS/SD, SD, SD/D and D) where large areas of potentially productive soils exist thus could be turned to the more effective service of man. This applies particularly to parts of Africa and Asia—but the coastal deserts and the inland arid sectors of Peru and Chile also could be developed further along these lines.

(*d*) Power certainly would be required—well distributed, abundant, economic in production and distribution—for pumping of water, perhaps for powered soil preparation by methods and means as yet not even imagined. Not only would this depend upon the development of the potential hydroelectric power of the three continents but also upon the possible use of nuclear power. At least one imaginative engineer and industrialist already has thought of the possibility and the value of simple compact and relatively cheap nuclear-fuelled stations of about 1000 kVA with supporting staff, in the wildernesses of the world (*vide Nature*, 14 November 1959).

It does not require much imagination to foresee the possible advantages of cheap and abundant power in great producing areas for activities such as large-scaled irrigation and drainage, the operating of processing plants and cooling installations, canning factories, breweries and distilleries, tanneries, textile mills and the like.

(*e*) The provision of satisfactory education, both general and in agriculture and other specialist disciplines at the appropriate levels, is essential to the training of better classes of cultivators, pastoralists, 'mixed' and irrigation farmers, and for the ensuring of a sufficiency of adequately trained administrative cadres, engineers, chemists and

artisans for the satisfactory operating of the associated industries.*
Research and extension personnel are among those most seriously
required in a world exerting efforts for the growing of crops, the
management of livestock and the development of freshwater and
marine fisheries.

(f) An additional support should be sought from the development
of special crops such as algae, freshwater and marine, for the provision of foods and other requirements organic and inorganic. The
work so far done on *Chlorella* is probably only an introduction to
great possibilities (*vide* Heywood (1956)). In the tropics and hotter
subtropics the freshwater algal growth should be luxuriant provided
suitable species or strains are selected for cultivation.

Assuming the foregoing conditions are met, there need be no fear
of the so-called 'population bomb' (Cook (1956) and similar uneasiness (Vannevar Bush (1956); Kipping (1959); Thompson (1959);
Lord Adrian (1959) and Macfarlane Burnet). But the meeting of these
conditions brooks no delay and makes demands which cannot be
satisfied readily, even if all the mental, moral, scientific, technical,
managerial and financial support essential be ensured. All measures
of encouragement and support included, it must be realized that the
fundamentally necessary requirement is the winning of the heart and
minds of the local leaders, the rank and the humble file of the rural
and related communities in the nearer and the remote districts of all
the countries involved, in efforts to prevent the shattering blast of
the 'population bomb'. This is one of the most challenging tasks
that men of goodwill in the highly developed and semi-developed
world could undertake.

(2) Experience gained by means of the Colombo Plan† and by
others interested in larger-scaled propositions in agricultural
development in South America and Africa reveals the great difficulties involved in the obtaining of adequate funds from abroad,
that is funds sufficient to enable the respective governments to go
ahead with really significant undertakings.

* This point is noted in an apt and timely manner by Eugene Black
(1960) in his address to the Economic and Social Council of U.N.O. Using
Africa as an example, but speaking more generally of underdeveloped
territories, he emphasizes the basic requirement for faster development
to be 'more education and training at all levels—a more generally literate
working force, more skilled artisans, more members of the learned profes-
sions, more entrepreneurs, more experienced government administrators '.

† *Vide* Benham (1956).

THE AIDING OF AGRICULTURAL DEVELOPMENT

The self-evident truth is becoming somewhat better understood —that money and men—technologists, artisans, semi-skilled and even ordinary labour—are not readily found by the countries in which assisted undertakings are to be developed. Sometimes this is due to inability, sometimes to lack of a sufficient sense of obligation and fortunately only rarely because of sheer political awkwardness. Again, the responses from the nationals of some countries have been poor both in amount and quality. Furthermore, some governments and other interests have not shown a wholehearted desire to contribute to the costs of development, either through funds obtainable by increased taxation or an effective provision of the sinews of development in the form of transport, power, water and agricultural and related activity. In short, the evidence so far is against self-help being considered a moral responsibility by some of the recipient and petitioning countries.

Whether a consistent shortage of funds from external sources will curtail expansion of really satisfactory dimensions will be proven when the United Nations Special Fund to finance large-scaled schemes of economic development in the underdeveloped countries is applied in the measure expected to be requisite. According to its director, Mr. Paul Hoffman, the Fund aims at doubling the increase of the income *per caput* in underdeveloped countries during the first decade. The United States is reported to be contributing funds of the order of 1600 million dollars for the first five years.

As an indication of the need of large injections of foreign capital, for many years to come, in order to maintain and accelerate the momentum of development where it is required, Eugene Black (1960) records that at the end of 1958 Latin America on the one hand and Asia, the Middle East and Africa on the other, had outstanding public debts of about 5 billion U.S. dollars, since when further debt expansion has occurred. This indebtedness is not considered excessive, but does indicate the magnitude of the values presently and potentially wanted. Agriculture and forestry of course directly have accounted for a relatively small proportion of the 5 billion dollars.*

* Her Majesty's Government in the U.K. (Treasury, Cmd. 974: 1960) is to be commended for the relatively large contributions made to the assistance of Development Overseas, 1951–60: £753 million, exclusive of military aid and refugee assistance. An unstated but certainly relatively small part of this has been for *direct* aid to Agriculture and Forestry; but *indirectly* these industries have been assisted considerably.

There is some possibility of an increasing proportion of the costs of development being found not from loans from international sources—such as the International Bank for Reconstruction and Development (I.B.R.D.), or, through the Bank, the International Finance Corporation (I.F.C.) established in 1956 and linked with the Bank and the International Development Association (IDA.)* established in 1960 and also to be linked with the Bank—but also by individual countries: the United States, the United Kingdom, Russia, Germany, France, the Netherlands, and some of the older Commonwealth countries. Belgium, despite her travail in the Congo in mid-1960, might be prepared to partake in this form of aid. †

But this possibility would require careful consideration lest matters of political nature be associated with the assistance in men, machines and money. 'Strings' of this kind should be avoided at all cost. A relatively small international organization providing for *bilateral* or *mutual* aid recently has been established in Trans-Saharan Africa, the Foundation for Mutual Assistance in Africa (F.A.M.A.), whereby member countries could aid each other through technical assistance, probably rarely, if ever, by funds. At present there are no special conditions attached to such *bilateral* aid.

Because of the lesser risk of political conditions becoming involved, it is advisable to attempt to finance development in the tropical and subtropical countries by means of *multilateral* aid through organizations like I.B.R.D., IDA. and the I.F.C., associated with the I.B.R.D. Myrdall (1956; 1958) is sound in advocating *multilateral* aid as contrasted with *bilateral*.

(3) It should be remembered that in the underdeveloped countries the stimulus for large-scale development invariably comes from

* The IDA. is a close affiliate of the I.B.R.D.; if all members of the Bank join IDA. its initial resources would be the equivalent of 1000 million U.S. dollars. The United Kingdom has contributed the equivalent of 131.14 million U.S. dollars and the United States 320.29 dollars. Twenty-two countries, by early November 1960, had contributed the equivalent of 726.72 million U.S. dollars, and other countries in Africa, Asia, Europe and Latin American had completed various stages of the procedure of membership.

† In December 1960 the United States, Britain, Canada and seventeen West European nations formed the Trans-Atlantic Organization for Economic Co-operation and Development. Replacing O.E.E.C., this new body begins work in Paris in September 1961 and aims at giving economic and technical assistance to the industrially underdeveloped countries of Latin America, Africa and Asia. (Q.E.C.D.)

above. For this reason there is a natural tendency to encourage not the gradual development of projects involving a large number of important and clearly viable minor propositions but rather undertakings of large and occasionally even grandiose dimensions, entailing comparatively immense expenditure. It is true, of course, that the small man has 'developed' certain crops in the fullness of time, e.g. rubber and coconut in Malaya and elsewhere, tea in various places and cocoa in West Africa. The reference here is not to this gradual form of development but to organised and usually large-scale development at a high tempo.

As regards grandiose propositions and, of course, also those of more sober nature, it should be appreciated that underdeveloped countries should not be permitted to undertake development plans in so care-free a manner as they appear to do. Their own resources must be examined impartially and with appropriate care, and there should be a definite agreement that in reasonable measure a proportion of these should contribute either directly or otherwise toward the costs of the projected development. If this kind of arrangement be not made and followed in spirit and in practice, there will recur the tendency for underdeveloped countries to import above their capacity for paying for such importations from the proceeds from their exports.

Related to the above point is the ensuring that the administration of assistance for development should aim always at the *continuity* of international trade. Countries contributing directly or otherwise to the development of the less privileged territories must be prepared to accept repayment not so much in currency transfers but more often in goods and perhaps, under special circumstances, services. This export of home-produced goods is of course vital to the routine servicing of investment.

Although what is known as *import substitution* (*vide* Black (1959A)) —that is the local production of commodities so as to eliminate or reduce their import—certainly is commendable where ecological and economic features favour the plant or animal products concerned, it still is basically correct that development should aim at *exports* so as to win foreign exchange.

(4) Agricultural development of course cannot yield early and large dividends, hence the repayment of funds loaned on the normal *hard loan* basis is usually most difficult. The probability that the new organization, IDA., may be able to furnish *soft loans* based on

much easier terms of repayment well might stimulate the financing of projects in crop and livestock production. Naturally the availability of these *soft loans* and their being placed at the disposal of the administrations of underdeveloped countries must presuppose the most careful scrutiny of the proposals made, a scrutiny both technical and economic. An official assurance also should be given that the management of the projects would be along acceptable lines. Furthermore it would be wise to arrange for frequent contact between representatives of the Bank or IDA., those of the administrations and the recipients.

Soft loans should be granted not only for the furtherance of subsistence production but also for the encouragement of export commodity production. It should be observed, however, that as the presently envisaged initial capital is one thousand million U.S. dollars, three-quarters of which would be available for loans over the first five years at the rate of about 150 million U.S. dollars per year, the most rigorous selection of development propositions would be necessary in the admittedly uncertain sphere of crop and livestock production. Black (1959B) rightly has stressed the wisdom of economic assistance being given rather for the production of *quality* than for quantity only.

Commencing with the comparatively modest finances available initially to IDA. and other organizations capable of investing capital in the development of tropical agriculture, it is to be hoped that in due time some well-directed stimulus will be given to sound policies and practices. It should be emphasized, however, that essential as capital is for this purpose, the capturing of the heart and mind of man in these regions is equally important. Local leadership and inspiration, helped at first where necessary by foreign personnel of proven ability and integrity, alone can supply the requisite continuing spirit. Without an abundance of this spirit in the local people the investment of foreign capital could never be employed to the best possible advantage.

(5) Like any other form of development that of agriculture and forestry cannot be made to order. Development naturally must emerge from the possibilities of the bioclimatic region and must be inspired by the desire and the capacity of *the man on the ground*. This high rating of the significance of the individual producer is intentional, because farming in essence is an individualistic enterprise even if conducted along team or co-operative lines.

It is obvious also that agricultural and forestry development cannot be considered as interests and activities apart: they build in with other forms of development and, to be successful, must be appropriately co-ordinated therewith. These kinds of development are never complete because they are never *static*, but like life itself they are for ever *dynamic*, and therefore must evolve with time and with the experience of those at the oar and the helm. This spark of the necessary *dynamism* in those who guide and labour in these kinds of development is mentioned again later when I deal with the nature of technical assistance.

(6) It should be remembered, also, that while political stability and all that accompanies this happy state of affairs—a sound administration and professional and other officials of ability and integrity beyond reproach—are conducive to sound agricultural development, this cannot of itself generate the spirit of development within the farming community or the individual 'man on the ground'. In a general connection Frankel (1952) has mentioned this point, which definitely is of direct application in the sphere of agricultural and associated development. The selection of viable projects, preferably of the minor kind in which the simple cultivator, farmer and pastoralist could join to their advantage, would go far toward sowing and culturing the seeds of interest in the rural communities. To this informed kind of demonstration the mundane but important matters of the organization of feeder roads and the improvement of distribution and marketing would add further value.

(7) It is true, of course, that the influence of the development of mining, industry and employment in the lower ranks of the public services operates together with the growing tempo of detribalization in drawing men and their dependants from the rural areas to the urban. Public amenities and health, a greater variety of food, the pleasures of recreation and the opportunities for education are among the attractions, no matter what the individual losses might be in moving from the country to the town. This move sometimes is regarded as wholly unhappy because of the lack of opportunities for worth-while employment in the towns, but sometimes rightly is well regarded where there is a dearth of unskilled and other labour for industry and other forms of employment in the urban areas. Where industrial and related development is capable of providing satisfactory employment, training and a way of life for people from the country, the flow towards the urban areas should be encouraged, so

as to relieve the usually overwhelming preponderance of people directly dependent upon agriculture. But this should be a regulated progress—and proverbially this regulating is a most difficult task even for the most experienced authorities.

A point of outstanding importance is that the 'drift to town' should be controlled and, perhaps, even reversed were there the necessity to develop more intensively some especially viable kind of agricultural undertaking. This control should be self-generated and therefore should require a minimum of official intervention, which of itself commonly is unsatisfactory sociologically and politically.

(8) From a study of the agricultural setting and the economy of a number of tropical countries there appears a strong reason for attempting to strike a suitable balance between an export commodity and a local cash production, on the one hand, and the provision of a sufficiency of food and other daily requirements on the other. It goes without saying that both production for export and that for subsistence must be conducted along lines certain to maintain, if not improve, the soil and water resources. Development propositions which stress the virtues of the production of export commodities also should do all that is economically possible to stimulate subsistence farming in the environs or as close thereto as feasible.

(9) *New patterns* of agricultural development introduced into countries, where for decades the *indigenous patterns* have yielded material for subsistence and perhaps also for local sale and export, are fraught with danger. Attempted introductions readily might fail, unless particularly sympathetic and experienced personnel direct the policy and the practice in the new *patterning*. Some examples are:

(*a*) Large-scaled crop production projects, either rain-fed or under irrigation, and either wholly or largely mechanized; probably directed from one or more centres of control, but depending upon the co-operation of the small cultivator and his family.

(*b*) Commodity crop farming—such as coffee, cocoa, tea, sugar, banana, oil-palm, rubber, copra, sisal and cotton—along progressive lines with the small cultivator and his patches of land as the basis.

(*c*) Large-scale communal livestock production, according to modern standards, so far as the climate, vegetation, type of animal and the experience and capacity of the local pastoralist permit.

(*d*) Intensive poultry production along scientific lines and employing high-producing exotic strains, demanding high standards of feeding, tending, general maintenance and veterinary attention:

173

either run as co-operative farming ventures or along 'estate' lines, but in either form making heavy demands upon the growing of a portion, at least, of the concentrates and necessitating the importation of those ingredients impossible to grow or purchase locally.

The inherent difficulty encountered in attempting to combine *traditional* and *introduced patterns* in general development has been noted by Frankel (1953), and this is found also in agricultural and associated development because of the essentially diverse approaches and practices usually essential in *introduced* patterns of agriculture.

Much as the tropical and hotter subtropical countries owe to European, British and—in Latin America, more particularly—American agricultural background, education, training, methods and machinery, I believe that in some senses we foreigners have failed to realize sufficiently early and clearly the extent to which we have attempted to grid our ideas upon the peoples of these regions. I have touched elsewhere upon the confusion introduced by the concept of neat, regularly espaced, clean-cultivated single-crop plantings as contrasted with the traditional irregular, weedy and mixed cultures, our attachment to the bringing in of exotic animals and the fenced paddock in livestock management and the like (Phillips, 1959B: 370). Let us be more careful, therefore, in the future not to make confusions worse confounded by pressing an admixture of indigenous and introduced notions upon the whole communities, unless we and they are aware of the probable or the certain economic and sociological implications. We must be humble in our anxiety to assist development: we know in part only, but at times we behave as though we were omniscient. (Re *Education*, *vide* Phillips (1960c; 1961).)

(10) Restricted portions of the humid and the arid tropics and hotter subtropics for a time may live up to the expectation of those who incline to value their richness, actual and potential, as theoretically the highest possible in the whole realm of crop production (*vide* National Academy of Sciences (1959)). But even in these more highly favoured localities the richness is evanescent, unless the most careful and able ways and means of conservation of the natural resources of the environment are applied throughout. But generally this over-optimistic impression simply is not supported by the bioclimatic, the edaphic and the economic facts.

It behoves all charged with guiding the development of the tropics and hotter subtropics for crop and livestock production to realize certain sober truths: (*a*) High-level richness of the soils is restricted

and is readily lost when these are given other than first-class management—especially in the raising of seasonal crops; (*b*) a fair proportion of the soils is of fair to mediocre quality only, the productivity
of which corresponds with this graded classification and is readily
lost unless the principles and practices of conservation be applied
with ability and experience; (*c*) the residue—a large proportion but
varying much locally according to the bioclimatic conditions and
physiography, is poor in every sense and, in the absence of either
drainage—where too humid and wet—or irrigation—where too arid
and dry—is low in productivity.

For those holding the purse-strings of technical assistance and
financial aid the arranging of loans even of the *softest* of the prospective *soft* terms, this realization should mean the exercising of the
very greatest of care in the assessment of the *promise* of the proposed
projects—*before they loosen the strings.* From my experience in
several parts of the regions discussed here and also from contacts
with some who know the local conditions intimately, I sense the
risks attending roseate impressions and optimistic estimation of the
practicability and the productivity of propositions of the kind
mentioned above. Only by careful study, *in situ*, supported by well-
planned and ably conducted pilot projects, would it be possible to
offer sound and firmly based guidance about the prospective viability
of the numerous propositions which today are advocated by politicians and very senior officials responsible for so-called agricultural
and associated development. The highly imaginative and grandoise
schemes usually are dismissible because of their not being based on
the elements of either agricultural or economic sense. (*Vide* Phillips
(1959B: 339; 366) *re* reasons for success or failure of large-scale
agricultural enterprises in Africa.)

(11) As our still meagre knowledge of the tropics and hotter
subtropics slowly grows the clearer does it become that the best
development of these, in agriculture—and where feasible, forestry—
will not be attained until much more efficient techniques and practices are evolved. This evolution in turn depends partly on a sound
understanding of the ecology of the gross and the local environment
—the micro-environment of specific localities under consideration
for development and, also, upon a satisfactory knowledge of the
sociological and the *psychological* patterns of the local human communities. For the rest, much more detailed information should be
gained about the responses of specific crops and kinds of livestock,

under diverse forms of management, to the environment and the micro-environment.

(12) Due to the many calls for guidance upon all the varied aspects of agricultural and forestry development the existing numbers of suitably experienced and capable advisers, investigators, specialists and extension and other field officers are unable to deal adequately with the demand.

Unfortunately this shortage inevitably has led to the employment of many who cannot accomplish at all well the varied and, at times, difficult tasks facing them. To some extent this is because of the comparatively restricted number of field officers and the even smaller one of specialists who have had a sufficiently long and wide experience in these regions. Indeed it is largely from the one-time Colonial services of Britain* and France and, in a lesser degree, of Holland that officers have been drawn in recent years for this international and national work. Due to her more recent overseas contacts with Latin America through her Foreign Agricultural Service, the United States has produced some personnel with comparable background, but for the greater part has depended upon field and specialist officers whose background largely has been American, and not always in the subtropical South.

Quite understandably the United States could not spare more than a small proportion of her more suitable officers for technical assistance service and, accordingly, has enlisted men without any specially appropriate experience and distinction. Some of these have done remarkably well, but many no more than could have been expected: they have understood neither the local agriculture and forestry nor the indigenous and naturalized cultivator, pastoralist and forester.

In light of what men from the former Colonial services and the United States services and universities have had to face and of the fine efforts some of these have made to grapple with awkward situations, it seems churlish to comment otherwise than gratefully about the current position. But thankful as all concerned should be for what has been attempted, it remains true that *too few* have had to advise on *too much* at *too high* a level in *too short* a time. It would be

* Much time was lost between 1950 and 1960 in the establishment of a pool of experienced overseas professional and other officers, available for service in the underdeveloped portions of the Commonwealth. At long last it seems as if something will be done to retain the services of these valuable officers. The British Government has been inordinately slow in seizing an opportunity for service.

surprising, therefore, if the best possible guidance had been given in the best possible manner at the best possible time on the best possible propositions.

At first it might appear irrelevant to discuss the present weaknesses of technical assistance in tropical and subtropical agriculture, forestry and related disciplines. A moment's examination should explain, however, the intimate link between technical assistance personnel, less informed than is desirable, and the quality of the guidance given not only to those responsible for deciding whether grants or loans should be made for particular purposes, but also to the territorial administrations, their professional officers and the rural communities.

At the risk of being tedious I am impelled to say that technical assistance can succeed only in the measure in which the personnel are in tune with the special needs of particular countries or communities. They must not be doctrinaire, but must possess the capacity for growing in mental ability and versatility with the study of the people and the problems they encounter. Furthermore, they must study and weigh not only the purely scientific and technical features of their problems and propositions but also must be acutely aware of the *economic*, the *sociological* and the *psychological* aspects of these.

Having seen technical assistance in operation for ten years in a range of countries from Latin America, through Africa, to South-East Asia—technical assistance provided by several international or overseas national organizations—I suggest that the whole of the subject of this kind of assistance demands careful overhaul and replanning—with special reference to the selection, the background and personality, the scientific, technical and administrative qualities, the intellectual and moral integrity and objectivity of the personnel. To agree upon how best to accomplish this review and to ensure that an early improvement in the number and quality of the personnel is practicable will not be easy, but should be the duty of men of wisdom carefully selected from international and national circles.

I welcome the establishment in June 1960 of the Overseas Development Institute, in London, to provide a centre of information on the *administrative* and *financial* aspects of development in countries where aid and guidance in development are desirable. Among the Institute's functions are to be the giving of advice as to the organizations and the channels through which aid is obtainable, and guidance as to the procedure and forms of development planning.

Apparently the Institute will *not* be concerned at all deeply with

177

the *technical* aspects: this is regrettable in light of all I have tried to say about the frailty of some of the technical assistance presently available. But perhaps the essential need of a study of these fundament matters—the *quantity* and the *quality* of technical aid—will appear in due time.

(13) During the tense times of the 'wind of change' in politics in the tropics and hotter subtropics it is significant that the new nationalism, in the minds of many people, has associated with it the risks, dangers and fears of unpredictable happenings. At present and for long to come Africa and Asia must be storm centres of political change even as Latin America was till not so long ago. This realization has introduced a tension locally and also far beyond the borders of many of the countries either already under 'new' administrations or shortly so to be. Tension of this kind patently is not conducive to sound, informed thought and forward planning in agriculture and forestry. We may expect more and not less tension.

It remains to be seen whether those responsible at the highest level for international finance and other aid could influence the leaders in countries of uneasy political balance to realize that political stability counts heavily in the world of economics and finance, and therefore, is essential to the granting of local assistance in the development of agriculture and forestry. If those in high office be not courteously frank about this vital matter they will have been guilty of forgetting the implications of *noblesse oblige*.

General Conclusions

Confining myself to the highlights of what has gone before, I believe the following conclusions to be justifiable and to warrant the earnest attention of all who assist in the development of the agriculture and the forestry of the tropics and the hotter subtropics:

(1) Undoubtedly these underdeveloped regions offer *promise* varying from good to mediocre and even poor, depending upon the bioclimatic, local soil, human and related characteristics. But they are *not* rich storehouses, consistently capable of high yields even from fairly well informed practices in agriculture and forestry. Their development along traditional and, under some circumstances, modern lines naturally is feasible, provided more is learned of their ecology; the potential revision of the *pattern* of their agriculture and,

where the bioclimatic conditions permit, their forestry; and the *pattern* of the sociology and psychology of their peoples.

(2) A serious need exists for informed, experienced and inspired technical assistance in the spheres of crop and livestock husbandry and production, soil and water conservation, co-operatives, communications, storage, processing, marketing and both general and detailed economics.

(3) Financially the amount of money which usefully could be invested even in a ten years' programme of development is vast and only rarely is likely to be forthcoming from external sources. The needs of the Congo will provide an impressive test of the realities of *altruistic* aid.

(4) For this reason serious efforts should be exerted by those responsible for grants and loans to be as *wisely selective* of propositions as possible. At the same time, all reasonable forms of suasion must play upon the administrations seeking aid, to generate financial, man-power and moral support for propositions that are accepted as worthy of trial by the prospective financiers. 'Today's aid . . . to-morrow's trade' must be supported by the inspiration that 'Fate helps those who help themselves!'

(5) Political stability, the provision of good public services—especially in administration, finance, law, health, education, and in the technical departments dealing with agriculture and forestry—and the encouragement of public and private investment by all practicable and honourable means, are fundamental to the satisfactory development of the rural communities. The *pattern* for this may be either traditional, but duly improved by modern experience, or along modern lines.

(6) Land-use surveys*, special economic survey missions, research, pilot projects and sound extension services in agriculture, forestry and soil and water conservation must precede and also accompany any national policy for development. Without these, in the appropriate setting and proportions, failure and disillusionment are inevitable.

(7) All who wish to see the underdeveloped sectors of the tropics and subtropics move toward more progressive and happier conditions in agriculture and forestry must have the consistent objective of the drawing out of the best that there is into the spirit of man in the rural

* *Vide* Pereira's (1959) views on a physical basis for land-use policies in tropical catchment areas, for an example of a valuable approach.

and related communities. Deeper than the brashness, perhaps inevitably associated temporarily with the 'new' independence, there is unquestionably in the 'new' nations the desire to acquit themselves well: a national pride of race and country and a burning desire to show what they can achieve.

(8) Wisely applied technical assistance and financial aid, closely intermeshed with these national aspirations, should make impressive inroads in the coming quarter of a century into the wildernesses of ignorance and of half-truths that presently retard progress in the development of agriculture and forestry.

Almost as if by inscrutable design, the United Nations and notably the United States, the Commonwealth and the French have been thrown the challenge and given the opportunity in the Congo. May they prove big enough for the occasion. So far, they have shown neither an intelligent grasp of the problem nor a determination to win the hearts and minds of the people. There has been a complete absence of the holistic or ecological approach to either the political or the economic problem of this storm-tossed country. But let us hope that this approach can still be made.

Funds from President Kennedy's Development Assistance Group (D.A.G.) with which Britain, the European 'Six', Canada, Portugal and Japan appear likely to be associated, might afford some aid to the rehabilitation of agriculture and other economies in this country presenting so great a challenge to all nations of good intention.

Appendix I

A Broad Comparison of Highly Developed, Semi-Developed and Underdeveloped Economies*

Status in terms of development	Highly developed	Semi-developed	Underdeveloped (Tropics and Hotter Subtropics)
Geographic distribution	United States, Canada, United Kingdom, France, Germany, Switzerland, Norway, Sweden, parts of Australia and New Zealand (parts of U.S.A., Canada and Australia still underdeveloped)	Portugal, Spain, Finland Italy, Greece, Turkey, Venezuela, Cuba, Chile, Argentine, Uruguay, Japan, Malaya, Union of South Africa (parts of all are underdeveloped)	All Central America, all South America except countries named as semi-developed; all West Indies except Cuba; all Africa except South Africa, all Asia except Malaya and Japan; Oceania except Australia
Approximate annual income per caput not including all subsistence won	Above 900 U.S. dollars (U.S.A. about 1500)	From 450–600 to 200–300; South American states named 450–600, Malaya 300–450, South Africa 200–300, Japan steadily rising: about 300–400 in 1957	Very largely under 100 U.S. dollars, but most of Central America 200–300, much of South America 200–300 (Peru, Paraguay 100–200), Federation of Rhodesia–Nyasaland and Egypt 100–200
Approximate calories intake per caput per diem; nutrition status	3000–3350–4000; very high to moderate	2500–2990; high to fair	Under 2500 (1000–1500 upwards); fair to low
Health of population and major problems	High standard public health; problems satisfactory	Locally high to generally very fair to fair; in tropics/subtropics malaria; provision for study very fair	Variable, often moderate, locally low; malaria, other tropical diseases and malnutrition major problems; provision for study from fair to poor
Proportion of world population involved	8 per cent (some proportion of population still poor)	About 12 per cent	45–50 per cent if Eastern bloc not included, 70–75 per cent if included
Population increase	Low (below 2 per cent)	2–3 per cent, high to moderate	High (over 2·5–3 per cent)

Status in terms of development	Highly developed	Semi-developed	Underdeveloped (Tropics and Hotter Subtropics)
Reduction in death rate	High reduction	High to moderate death rate, but reducing	Very high to high death rate, but reducing
Birth control	Conscious planning becoming commoner except in certain religious circles	In tropics/subtropics negligible	Nil to negligible, so far as is known, but attempts being made in parts of Asia
Proportion of population employed in agriculture, pastoral industry, gathering of food and fishing	Varies from about 11–20 per cent (U.S.A.) to 5 per cent (U.K.)	Variable, 19 (Uruguay) to 69 per cent (South Africa); South American states 38–40 per cent	Variable: 60 to over 90 per cent
Proportion of population employed in industrial, commercial and related activities	Very high	Locally fairly high, in general moderate to low	Locally moderate, widely very low
Proportion of potential crop land still undeveloped	Usually limited, but still appreciable in U.S.A. and Australia	Variable but in tropics/subtropics high to fairly high	Variable; relatively high as in parts of South America, Africa, to low as in India and some other parts of Asia
Estimated land hunger where population is very great	Not applicable because of relative smallness of rural proportion of population	In tropics/subtropics on increase but not yet serious	Slight in parts of South America, much of Africa (except parts of South Africa, Ruanda-Urundi, Nile Valley) to high in India and some other parts of Asia
Standard of agricultural and related production	Very high (U.K. and Europe) to high (U.S.A., Canada, New Zealand) to fairly high	Variable, from high to fair locally, low more widely	Variable, locally fair to mediocre, but widely low to very low
Standard of individual productivity in agriculture and related activities; proportion of mechanization	Very high to high; highly to fairly highly mechanized	Variable, from locally high to widely moderate to low; mechanization locally fairly high, generally increasing	Low to very low; little mechanization except very locally to locally
(1) Standard of elementary education in general and proportion of literacy (2) University education; proportion of	(1) High to fairly high; very high to high (2) Relatively high to moderate	(1) Variable, locally high to fairly high, more widely moderate to low; moderate (2) Moderate	(1) Low to very low except very locally; low to very low (2) Mainly very low, but locally high in parts of Asia

APPENDIX I

Pattern of income, savings, capital formation, investment	Income high, savings high to fairly high, high rate of capital formation and investment	Locally income high, savings high, fair rate of capital formation and investment, but widely all these moderate to low	Income low to very low, savings nil to negligible by general public; indigenous capital formation and investment low to negligible
Rate of economic growth	Very high to high to fairly high	Variable, locally high, widely moderate to fairly low	Very low, except very locally; usually due to expatriate influences, but exceptions in South America, West Africa
Proportion of the local economy under influence of world market conditions	Very high	Locally very high, widely moderate to low for agricultural export commodities	Low
Effort to stimulate industries and skills other than those requisite to filling export needs	Not directly applicable, but stimulation of skill very high	In tropics/subtropics variable, locally high; more widely moderate (Malaya, South Africa)	Hitherto slight but now improving because of changed political setting
Nature of tenure of arable and pastoral land	Normally individual tenure	Variable, locally in tropics/subtropics individual, but communal common	Frequently communal, with local examples of individual tenure; a tendency to encourage individual tenure locally under special circumstances
Research in agriculture and related fields	Highly progressive	In tropics/subtropics becoming more progressive ; locally as in South Africa, highly progressive	Recently slight to negligible, now improving in scope and quality
Extension of agricultural and related knowledge	Excellent to good to very fair	In tropics/subtropics fair to mediocre, but in South Africa good	Recently slight to negligible, improving
Education in agriculture and related subjects	Excellent to good	In tropics/subtropics fair to mediocre; but in South Africa moderate	Recently slight to negligible, improving
Conservation of soil, water and vegetation	Progressively good	In tropics/subtropics fair to mediocre; in South Africa locally good	Widely mediocre to negligible, locally good to fair in Federation of Rhodesia and Nyasaland, improving in parts of India

183

Note: The classification by countries naturally is not wholly satisfactory and, indeed, can be misleading because some parts of a country might be semi-developed but others underdeveloped. Moreover cities in underdeveloped countries usually show features of high development whereas the rural areas do not. The tabular statement could be challenged in detail at various points, hence it is necessary to emphasize that it purports to give a very broad comparison of the three economies only and *cannot be considered an attempt at precision.*

Appendix II

A Gross Comparison of the Classifications of Finch, Trewartha *et al.* (1957) and Phillips (1959b) as applied to the Tropics and Hotter Subtropics

Finch, Trewartha et al.	Phillips

(A) Tropical Humid Climates
(mean temperature of coolest months above 64·4° F. (18° C.))
    Af: Tropical Wet (Rainforest)*
	Highly Humid, Humid and Other Tropical Forest Bioclimates
	
	    HHF: Highly humid forest and
	    HF: Humid forest
	    HSF: Humid-subhumid forest

Am: Tropical Wet (Rainforest,† windward coast and Monsoon†)	HHF: Highly humid forest and
	    HF: Humid forest
	    HSF: Humid-subhumid forest
	    HMF: Humid montane forest and
	    HSMF: Humid-subhumid montane forest

Aw: Tropical Wet-and-Dry (savanna) (dry season(s)) in winter‡ for the hemisphere	SHWS: Subhumid tropical wooded savanna (MSAWS: Mild subarid wooded savanna, or SAWS: Subarid wooded savanna the equivalent in places)
As: As above, but dry season(s) in summer§ * f: feucht: humid, all the year, no month below 2·4 inches rain † m: monsoon controlled ‡ w: dry season(s) in winter § s: dry season in summer	As above

B) Dry Climates (evaporation greater than precipitation)
    BS: Semiarid or Steppe*
    BSh: Tropical and Subtropical Steppe†
    BShw: Tropical and Subtropical Steppe (dry season in winter)‡
    BW: Arid or Desert§
	MSAWS: Mild subarid wooded and
	    SAWS: Subarid wooded savanna
	    AWS: Arid wooded savanna
	
	    AWS: Arid wooded savanna and
	    AWS/SD: Arid wooded savanna transitional to Subdesert

BWh: Tropical and Subtropical Desert
    BWn: Tropical and Subtropical Desert with frequent mist‖
	SD: Subdesert and
	    D: Desert, with SD/D as transition from Subdesert to Desert

* S: Steppe † h: heiss: hot, annual temperature above 64·4° F. (18° C.) ‡ w: dry season in winter § W: Wuste: desert ‖ n: nebel: mist	

(C) Humid Mesothermal Climates
    Caf: Humid Subtropical/warm summer, moist all the year*†
    Caw: Humid Subtropical, dry in winter‡
* f: feucht: humid, all the year
† a: mean temperature of warmest month above 77·1° F. (22° C.)
‡ w: dry season in winter
	Subtropical* Higher Montane
	HMF and HSMF, in places SHWS
	
	HMF and HSMF
	* ST: Subtropical

(H) Undifferentiated Highlands	HMF, HSMF (occasionally montane grassland, macchia, etc.)

184

Appendix III

A GENERAL COMPARISON OF HABITAT FACTORS AND HAZARDS FOR THE MAJOR BIOCLIMATIC REGIONS OF THE TROPICS AND HOTTER SUBTROPICS ACCORDING TO PHILLIPS'S CLASSIFICATION

So as to give a general impression of the principal characteristics of the major bioclimatic regions—their factors and hazards—these are summarized:

Bioclimatic region	Radiation*	Humidity†	Rain‡	Drought§	Saturation deficit in dry seasons	Wind	Evaporation
HHF: HIGHLY HUMID FOREST—low and medium elevations	megatherm, range very slight; monotonously uniform throughout year	uniformly high, range very slight	very high to high reliable, locally excessive	nil to very slight; EDM: 0–(1–2)	negligible	warm, highly humid	negligible to slight under canopy, moderate (to high) on extensive exposed areas; less than rain
HF: HUMID FOREST —low and medium elevations	megatherm, but above 2500–3000 feet mega-meso-therm; range very slight throughout year	uniformly high, with slight decrease in driest months and on drier days only	very high to high, normally reliable	short and mild, but locally may be longer and more severe; EDM: 1–2–3 (4), rarely more	slight to very slight to negligible	warm, humid, rarely seasonally humid-subhumid	slight under canopy, moderate (to high) on extensive exposed areas; less than rain
HSF: HUMID-SUBHUMID FOREST (a less humid variant of HF)—low and medium elevations	megatherm, but above 2500–3000 feet mega-meso-therm; range slight in rains, in drier seasons moderate	high except in drier months, when moderate	high (very high locally); reliable to locally less so	longer than HF, may be moderate to severe; EDM: 3–4–5–(6)	slight to moderate in EDM's	warm, humid, seasonally humid-subhumid	as for HF in moist months; in EDM's rather higher under canopy and moderate under full exposure; slightly greater than rain or equal thereto

185

Bioclimatic region	Radiation*	Humidity†	Rain‡	Drought§	Saturation deficit in dry seasons	Wind	Evaporation
HMF: HUMID MONTANE FOREST (with a less humid variant HSMF: HUMID-SUBHUMID MONTANE FOREST)—4000–10,000 ft.	mesotherm, range moderate (rarely high)	high, but in driest coolest months moderate	moderate to high, locally moderate; reliable	short to moderate; EDM: 3-4 (5) but locally less; 1-2	slight to moderate	cool to mildly warm, humid to humid-subhumid, may be strong	slight under canopy, moderate under full exposure (temporarily high when wind strong); about equal to rain
SHWS: SUBHUMID WOODED SAVANNA—low, medium and upland elevations	megatherm, but at higher elevations (3000 ft. upward) mega-mesotherm; range moderate to great according to rainy and dry seasons	high in rains, moderate in dry seasons	moderate to high; reliable so to fairly so to unreliable	moderate to fairly long and fairly severe to mild; EDM: (3)-4-5	moderate to to high	warm to hot, seasonally humid to subhumid, some seasons dry and cool	(moderate) to high in dry season, moderate in rains; greater than rain
MSAWS: MILD SUBARID WOODED SAVANNA: TRANSITIONAL BETWEEN SHWS AND SAWS: SUBARID WOODED SAVANNA—low, medium upland elevations	megatherm with variations as in SHWS	high in rains, moderate in dry season	much as SHWS but rather less rain (moderate), lower reliability	moderate to fairly long and fairly severe; EDM: 4-5-6	moderate to high	warm to hot, much as in SHWS	(moderate) to high in dry seasons, moderate in rains; greater than rain
SAWS: SUBARID WOODED SAVANNA—low, medium and upland elevations	megatherm, with variations as in SHWS, but range greater	high in rains, moderate in dry season	slight to moderate according to locality and year, unreliable	(moderate) to fairly long to (long) and fairly severe; EDM: (5)-7	high	warm to hot, rather drier than in SHWS—especially in dry season	high in dry seasons, moderate in rains, greater than rain
AWS: ARID WOODED SAVANNA—low, medium and upland elevations	megatherm, with variations as in SHWS, but range much greater	moderate to high in rains, slight in dry season	very slight to slight, unreliable	(fairly long) to long, and fairly severe to severe; EDM: 6-8	high to (very high)	as for SAWS but drier; may be cooler seasonally	high to (very high) in dry seasons, moderate in rainy; greater than rain
SD: SUBDESERT (in places WOODED SAVANNA)—low, medium and upland elevation (coastal variants may be more humid, but rain is negligible)	megatherm with variations as in SHWS, but range great to very great in dry season	moderate to high in rains, slight in dry season; drier than AWS	very, very slight to very slight, very unreliable	long to very long, severe to very severe, EDM: 7-10	high to very high	(warm) to hot, very dry in dry season; may be cooler seasonally	very high to (excessive locally)—in dry season but (moderate) to high in rains; much greater than rain

Climate type	Temperature / light	Humidity†	Rain‡	Drought§ (EDM's)	Atmospheric moisture	Temperature conditions	Radiation*
D: DESERT—low, medium and upland elevations (coastal variants are more humid, but rain negligible)	megatherm, range very great in dry season	moderate to high in rains, slight otherwise, drier than SD	nil to negligible to trace, to very, very slight, erratic	excessive and very severe; EDM: 10-11-(12)	excessive where not tempered, prior to and after rain, and along coasts	hot, very dry, but cooler seasonally	very high to excessive (coastally: high), high in rains; very much greater than rain
H: HOTTER SUB-TROPICAL (ST) VARIANTS include: HF-ST: Humid Forest HMF-ST: Humid Montane Forest SHWS-ST: Sub-humid Wooded Savanna MSAWS-ST: Mild Subarid Wooded Savanna SAWS-ST: Subarid Wooded Savanna AWS-ST: Arid Wooded Savanna SD-ST: Subdesert D-ST: Desert	The temperature is lower in all the subtropical variants, except at times in summer, in the AWS, the SD and the D; light intensities are usually high due to clearer skies, especially in the SAWS to D regions; in coastal deserts fog may be frequent	Usually less humid, region for region, than the tropical equivalents	Usually less rain than in tropical equivalents	Normally well-marked dry seasons; moderately severe to severe, sometimes with frost (except in HF, HMF; where the dry seasons are moderate in length and are not severe): EDM's of the order: HFST: 0-1-(2); HMF-ST: (3)-(4)-4-5-; MSAWS-ST: 4-5-(6); SAWS-ST: 5-6; AWS-ST: 6-7-(8); SD-ST: (7)-9-10-(11); D-ST: 9-11-(12)	In HF and HMF not significant; in SHWS moderate; in SAWS and AWS high; in SD high to very high; in D very high except in coastal types	Warm, humid in HF; cool, humid in HMF; in SHWS, MSAWS, SAWS, warm, moderately dry; in SD warm, dry; in D hot, very dry except when near coasts	Low to moderate under full exposure HF and HMF; in SHWS, MSAWS, SAWS moderate; in AWS, SD high, in D, except coastal types, high to very high; ratio to rain as for equivalent tropical bioclimatic regions

187

* *Radiation:* heat-light complex.
  Megatherm: above mean of 74° F. (23° C.).
  Mesotherm: mean of 68–74° F. (20–23° C.).

† *Humidity:*

	millibars
very high	above 27
high	20–27
moderate	13–20
slight	below 13

‡ *Rain:*

	inches
excessive	above 98; may attain over 200
very high	71–98
high	55–71
moderate	39–55
slight	24–39
very slight	16–24
very, very slight	8–16
trace	4–8
negligible	below

§ *Drought:*

	ecologically dry months (EDM's) (1 inch and less)
negligible	below 1 month
very short	1–2
short	3
moderate	4–5
fairly long	6
long	7
very long	8–9
excessive	10–12

Notes:

( ) indicates occasional, not usual.
Suffix –ST indicates *Subtropical.*

The symbols noted in Appendix II, HH (highly humid); H (humid); HSH (humid to humid-subhumid); F (forest); M (mild); S (sub); A (arid); WS (wooded savanna); SD (subdesert); D (desert); (transition, e.g. SD/D), apply throughout for Appendixes III and IV and elsewhere in text.

Appendix IV

THE MAJOR BIOCLIMATIC REGIONS OF THE TROPICS AND THE HOTTER SUBTROPICS: LATIN AMERICAN‖, AFRICAN, ASIAN, ACCORDING TO THE CLASSIFICATIONS OF FINCH, TREWARTHA *et al.* (1957) AND PHILLIPS (1959B)

The broadest classification of the larger bioclimatic regions alone is attempted. Students of local regions will find generalizations regarding areas which their more precise knowledge of specific conditions would lead them to subdivide or reclassify.

REFERENCES

* N.: North; S.: South; E.: East; W.: West.
† *Vide* map for more detail; a much contracted comparison is given in this column.
‡ For greater detail for Africa *vide* map in Phillips (1959B).
§ 'forest' shown thus is not true forest but scrub or wooded savanna; *vide* M. D. Chaturvedi (1956), after Champion (1936).

Country	Finch, Trewartha et al.	Phillips†
LATIN AMERICA ¶: MEXICO (from 30° N.,* southward)	H (conifer in part) Aw Bsh Af	HSF SHWS SAWS, AWS, SD HF (Mangrove E. and S. coasts)
GUATEMALA	H (conifer in part, centre) Af Aw (including deciduous scrub forest on W. coast, merging into *coniferous forest* inland)	HSF HHF/HF SHWS and HSF
EL SALVADOR	Aw (including deciduous scrub forest) H (conifer in part)	SHWS HSF
BRITISH HONDURAS	Af	HHF/HF (Mangrove S. coast, with an inlier of wooded savanna, SHWS/ HSF)

‖ L. R. Holdridge's classification (mean temperature values approximatilg those of the growing season and mean annual rainfall are plotted *logarithmically*) outlined in *Science*, 4th April 1947, has been applied by J. Tosi in Peru and by others elsewhere in Latin America. The method has some highly commendable features.
¶ *Vide* U.S.D.A.:F.A.S. (1958) for valuable maps used as part basis for map of bioclimatic regions in Latin America.

APPENDIX IV

Country	Finch, Trewartha et al.	Phillips†
HONDURAS	Aw (W. coast) H (centre) Af (E. coast)	SHWS HSF (conifer) HHF/HF (Mangrove E. coast)
NICARAGUA	Aw (W.) H (centre) Af (E. and S.)	SHWS (deciduous scrub and thorn) HSF (conifer) HHF/HF (extensive) (Mangrove E. coast)
COSTA RICA	Aw (W.) H (central) Af (E.)	SHWS HSF HHF/HF (Mangrove E. coast)
PANAMA	Aw (W. coast) Af (E. coast)	SHWS HHF/HF (Mangrove E. and W. coasts)
COLOMBIA	Af (interior, E. and S., very extensive) Af (Pacific coast) H Aw (N.)	HHF/HF HF HMF in part only (mainly *puna* and *tola* at higher elevations) SHWS (scrub, deciduous) and wooded savanna
ECUADOR	BS (Pacific coast) BWn Pacific (coast) H Af (extensive)	AWS/SD SD/D HMF (restricted) and alpine vegetation HHF/HF

189

Country	Finch, Trewartha et al.	Phillips†
PERU	BWh (Pacific coast) H (lengthy and wide)	SD/D At lower levels restricted HMF, at higher elevations (*paramos*, *puna* and *tola*)
	Af (Amazon; very extensive)	HHF/HF, with swamp forest, riverine forest and related types
VENEZUELA (from N. to S.)	—	Mangrove
	BWh (coastal fringe in N.) Aw (extensive) Af (S.)	SAWS SHWS HF
BRITISH GUIANA	Am (coastal fringe, N.E.) Aw (inland)	HHF/HF HF (interior sector is SHWS or induced wooded savanna derived from HF(?))
SURINAM	— Am (entire country)	Mangrove HHF merging into HF in interior
FRENCH GUIANA	— Am (entire country)	Mangrove HHF/HF
BRAZIL	Af (N.W. extensive)	HHF, with HF in some localities
	Am (N.E. and E.) Aw (vast expanse, extending to E. coast and far to S.) BSh (restricted area in E.) Caf (S.E. sectors) with some Cb (evergreen and deciduous forest)	HF (Selva) SHWS and probably drier variants SAWS/AWS HF (subtropical)

Country	Finch, Trewartha et al.	Phillips†
BOLIVIA (W. to E.)	H (broad, extensive)	HMF restricted and at lower elevations, mainly *paramos* at highest
	Caf (small sector, in S.W. corner)	HF (subtropical)
	Aw (inland, extensive, linking with the vast Aw of Brazil)	SHWS merging in SAWS/AWS in parts; with large swamp grassland areas and palm savanna
	Af (N., on Peru/Brazil borders, small sector)	HHF
PARAGUAY	BS (N.)	AWS
	Caf (N. and W.)	SHWS
	(S.E. sector)	HF (subtropical)
AFRICA (*Tropics and Hotter Subtropics*).‡ (Where necessary, individual countries are detailed in text):		
WEST AFRICA: MAURITANIA to NIGERIA/ CAMEROONS (from S. to N.)	— Am	Mangroves extensive HHF/HF, with HF more extensive and local areas of HMF
	BSh (coastal)	HSF (local)/SHWS
	Aw (very extensive S. to N. and W. to E.)	SHWS, MSAWS and SAWS in very roughly banded sequence from S. to N.
	BShW (extensive (W. to E.))	SAWS (northern portions)/AWS with some milder SD in far N.
	BWh (vast)	SD and D

Country	Finch, Trewartha et al.	Phillips†
EQUATORIAL AFRICA (mainly former FRENCH EQUA-TORIAL AFRICA: A.E.F. from GABON northward)	Aw (W. coast to former Belgian Congo border on E.)	HHF/HF, with HF more extensive
	Af (N. of the above)	HHF/HF with HHF more extensive, with some swamp forest and some *induced* wooded savanna formerly HHF and HF; vast expanse of HHF/HF and induced wooded savanna
	Aw (to N. of Af above); from E. border of Nigeria eastward and to N. of former Belgian Congo to Sudan western border; very extensive	Much former HF, now *induced* wooded savanna, and SHWS
	BShW (to N. of Aw above, extensive)	SAWS and SAWS/AWS transition and AWS
	BWh (to N. of BShW above; very extensive)	AWS/SD, SD/D
Former BELGIAN CONGO (S. to N.)	Aw (very extensive; S., S.W. and S.E.)	SHWS further S., but N. much relict HF and *induced* wooded savanna
	Af (vast; northward, westward and eastward, extending to almost northern border)	HHF, with much local *Swamp Forest*
	Aw (very narrow fringe near northern border; continuous with wide belt in Niger)	HF relics and *induced* wooded savanna, a narrow zone
	H (undifferentiated highlands)	HMF and some HSMF
SUDAN (S. to N.)	—	SHWS (local) and HMF (local: Imatong) a zonation from S. to N.: SHWS/MSAWS/SAWS/AWS
	B Shw (vast)	
	BWh (vast)	SD/D, with D in N.

APPENDIX IV

Country	Finch, Trewartha et al.	Phillips†
ETHIOPIA (S. to N.)	BWh (S. to E.) BShw (S.W. toward S.E.) H BShw (N.W. and N. of H): small area BWh (E. of H, toward ocean; narrow)	SD/D, SD AWS/MSAWS/ SHWS from S.W. to N.E. SHWS/HSMF/HMF and *induced* wooded savanna with forest relics AWS/SD, SD/D SD and SD/D
SOMALI REPUBLIC (S.W. to N.E.)	(in S.E. coastal area) BWh (most of Somalia and S.E. sector of Somaliland) BShw (W. sector, Somaliland) —	SAWS/AWS AWS and AWS/SD, SD and SD/D AWS HSMF local in Somaliland, set in MSAWS, restricted
BRITISH EAST AFRICA: TANGANYIKA (S. to N.)	Aw (for almost all the territory, except for two minor climatic areas): BSh (minor coastal strip in S.E.) H (around Kilimanjaro and related mountains; and on border with former Belgian Congo; restricted)	Mangroves, extensive irregular areas and zones of SHWS, MSAWS, SAWS, AWS—with local restricted areas of HF and HMF and HSMF SHWS and MSAWS HMF and HSMF
KENYA (S. to N.)	Aw (from coast inland, in irregular zonation) H BSh BWh (E. and N.)	MSAWS, AWS, SHWS HMF, HSMF, SHWS and much *induced* wooded savanna SD/AWS and AWS SD and SD/AWS, and in N. SD/D

13 193

APPENDIX IV

Country	Finch, Trewartha et al.	Phillips†
PORTUGUESE EAST AFRICA: MOÇAMBIQUE (S. to N.)	BSh (S.W. extreme, restricted)	Mangrove frequent AWS
	Aw (most of country)	MSAWS, SHWS, extensive, with local HF (nearer coast) and HMF and HSMF
	BSh (restricted area on W. boundary with S. Rhodesia)	AWS
BECHUANALAND PROTECTORATE (S. to N.)	BW (S.W. corner) BSh (most of country)	SD AWS (narrow), AWS/SD (narrow), SD (extensive) in succession from E. to W.
FEDERATION OF RHODESIA AND NYASALAND (S. to N.): SOUTHERN RHODESIA	BSh (much of the country)	AWS and SAWS (Limpopo to Zambezi)
	Aw (in N.E., fair area)	MSAWS, MSAWS/SAWS with restricted and local HMF and HSMF and *induced* wooded savanna and grassland
	BSh (narrow tongue between Aw in S. Rhodesia and Aw in N. Rhodesia, along border of S./N. Rhodesia)	AWS, SAWS
NORTHERN RHODESIA	BSh (as for BSh above) Aw (remainder of country)	AWS, SAWS AWS (extensive) MSAWS, SHWS (extensive)
NYASALAND	Aw H	MSAWS, SHWS HMF and *induced* wooded savanna

APPENDIX IV

Country	Finch, Trewartha et al.	Phillips†
PORTUGUESE WEST AFRICA: ANGOLA (W. to E.)	BWh (coastal strip)	D (D/SD near S. border but beyond Luanda, SD/AWS)
	BSh (narrow strip inland of BWh above)	SD/AWS
	Aw (remainder, vast)	SHWS extensive, with narrow strip MSAWS in S.; local HMF in high elevations, relics of greater areas, now *induced* grassland
	—	HF (relics) and much *induced* wooded savanna in N. (Cabinda)
SOUTH-WEST AFRICA (W. to E.)	BWh (coastal strip and S.E.)	D, D/SD, SD
	BSh (remainder, extensive)	AWS, with a strip of SAWS in far N.
SWAZILAND	Cbw (W. portion)	MSA/SH *induced* grassland and relic HMF and HSMF
	Caf (E. portion)	SAWS
MADAGASCAR (W. to E.)	BSh (S.–W.)	SAWS
	Aw (centre)	SHWS/MSAWS
	Af (E.)	HHF/HF
	—	Mangroves W. and E. coasts—local
ASIA: PAKISTAN (S.E. to N.W.): West:	—	Scattered '*dry*' (hill) and '*plains*', 'forests' (along rivers)
	BSh	SD and AWS
	BWh	SD, with D in part
East:	Aw (W.)	SHWS
	Am (E.)	HF and HHF
	—	Mangroves and tidal forests

195

Country	Finch, Trewartha et al.	Phillips†
INDIA (W. to E., N. of Tropic of Cancer)	BWh	AWS (xerophytic 'forest' of Chaturvedi (1956)§
	BSh	SHWS/MSAWS (dry 'forest', Chaturvedi)
	Caw (extensive)	HSF (subtropical) (monsoon forest, Chaturvedi)
	Am	HHF/HF
INDIA (S. of Tropic of Cancer)		HHF/HF (rain forest of Chaturvedi)
	Am	HF/HSF (narrow strip, monsoon forest, Chaturvedi)
	Aw (narrow strip)	SHWS
	BSh	AWS (xerophytic 'forest' of Chaturvedi)
	BSh and Aw (central, extensive)	SHWS/MSAWS (dry 'forest' of Chaturvedi)
	Aw (eastern, extensive) (with some Caw)	HSF and SHWS (monsoon forest of Chaturvedi)
	As (E. coast, S. of Aw above; dry season in summer)	SHWS and in moister areas HSF
	—	Swamp forests and Mangrove
CEYLON	Am (S. and S.W., 'wet zone')	HHF, HF and HMF
	As (dry season in summer) 'dryzone'	SHWS and HSF (in moister areas further S. in the dry zone)
BURMA (W. to E.)	Am	HHF/HF
	Aw	SHWS and *induced* wooded savanna
	—	Mangroves and swamp forest (Irrawady)
	Caw (to N. of Aw)	HSF (subtropical)

APPENDIX IV

Country	Finch, Trewartha et al.	Phillips†
THAILAND (W. to E.)	— Am (narrow belt) Aw	Mangrove HHF/HF SHWS and *induced* wooded savanna, extensive derived from HF and perhaps HSF
MALAYA	— Af	Mangrove and swamp forest, coastal HHF/HF Includes HMF in higher elevations Includes inland swamp forests
INDO-CHINA (Southern: CAMBODIA and VIET-NAM): CAMBODIA	— Af (W. coast) small area Aw (inland, to E.) extensive	Mangrove and swamp forests, coastal HHF/HF, and at higher elevations, a form of HF or HMF SHWS and some *induced* wooded savanna, derived perhaps from HF
VIET-NAM	— Af (W. of coastal strip) Aw	Mangrove and swamp forests, coastal HHF SHWS and *induced* wooded savanna, derived perhaps from HF
INDONESIA: SUMATRA	— Af	Mangroves and swamp forest, coastal HHF/HF including HMF on an interrupted spine inland, on W. side

197

Country	Finch, Trewartha et al.	Phillips†
JAVA	—	Mangroves/swamp forests, coastal
	Af	HHF/HF, with some HSF on E. side
	Aw	HSF and *induced* wooded savanna on E. side
BORNEO	—	Mangroves and coastal swamps
	Af	HHF/HF, with some HMF
	H	HMF
BRITISH NORTH	—	Mangroves
BORNEO: BRUNEI	Af	HHF/HF
and SARAWAK	H	HMF
PHILIPPINES	—	Mangroves
	Af	HHF/HF including some HMF locally

Appendix V

MAGNITUDE AND OBJECTS OF LOANS PROVIDED BY THE WORLD BANK FOR AGRI-
CULTURAL AND RELATED DEVELOPMENT WITHIN CERTAIN TROPICAL-SUBTROPICAL
COUNTRIES

An indication of the magnitude and the objects of the loans provided by the World Bank, since its inception in 1947, for the furtherance of agricultural and related development, in its *narrower* sense, within the tropical-subtropical countries included in this study, is obtained from Tables I and II.   The information is based upon records kindly supplied by the World Bank (1960B).

TABLE I

SUMMARY OF WORLD BANK LOANS FOR THE FURTHERANCE OF AGRICULTURE (IN-
CLUDING LAND RECLAMATION AND IRRIGATION) AND FOREST INDUSTRY IN THE
TROPICS AND HOTTER SUBTROPICS: 1947 TO JUNE 1960

Borrower and guarantor	Programme or project	Date	Maturities	Interest rate including commission (per cent)	Original principal amount in millions U.S. dollars
BELGIUM Belgian Congo (Congo Republic)	Agricultural development	Mar. 1960	1964–72	6	7·0
CHILE Fomento	Agricultural development	Mar. 1948	1950–5	$3\frac{3}{4}$	2·5
Fomento	Exploration for and use of water	Oct. 1951	1955–61	$4\frac{5}{8}$	1·3
Fomento	Construction of paper and pulp mills	Sept. 1953	1958–70	5	20·0
COLOMBIA Caja de Credito	Agricultural development	Aug. 1949	1952–6	$3\frac{1}{2}$	5·0
Caja de Credito	Agricultural development	Dec. 1954	1957–61	$4\frac{1}{4}$	5·0
COSTA RICA Banco Central du Costa Rica	Agricultural development and light industry	Sept. 1956	1958–63	$4\frac{3}{4}$	3·0
		Feb. 1959	1960–5	$5\frac{3}{4}$	3·5
INDIA	Agricultural development	Sept. 1949	1952–6	$3\frac{1}{2}$	10·0
	Damodar multi-purpose project	Jan. 1953	1956–77	$4\frac{7}{8}$	19·5
NICARAGUA	Construction of grain storage facilities	Oct. 1951	1954–62	$4\frac{3}{8}$	0·55
NICARAGUA Banco Nacional de Nicaragua	Agricultural development	Jun. 1951	1954–8	4	1·2
Instituto de Fomento Nacional	Agricultural development	Aug. 1955	1957–67	$4\frac{1}{4}$	1·5
PAKISTAN	Agricultural development	Jun. 1952	1954–9	$4\frac{1}{4}$	3·25
PAKISTAN Karnaphuli Paper Mills Ltd.	Construction of paper and pulp mill	Aug. 1955	1956–70	$4\frac{5}{8}$	4·2
PANAMA	Agricultural development	Sept. 1953	1955–60	$4\frac{5}{8}$	1·2
Instituto de Fomento Economico	Construction of grain storage facilities	Sept. 1953	1955–61	$4\frac{5}{8}$	0·29
PARAGUAY	Agricultural development	Dec. 1951	1954–64	$4\frac{3}{8}$	5·0
PERU	Agricultural development	July 1952	1954–9	$4\frac{1}{4}$	1·3
	Agricultural development	Apr. 1954	1956–61	$4\frac{1}{4}$	1·7
	Irrigation project	Apr. 1955	1959–80	$4\frac{3}{4}$	18·0

APPENDIX V

Borrower and Guarantor	Programme of project	Date	Maturities	Interest rate including commission (per cent)	Original principal amount in millions U.S. dollars

PERU
Banco de
  Fomento
  Agropecuario
	Agricultural development
	Agricultural development
	Agricultural development
		Nov. 1954
		Mar. 1957
		Jun. 1960
			1957–63
			1959–65
			Amortization begins June 1963
				4¼
				5½
				6
					5·0
					5·0
					5·0

SUDAN	Irrigation, completing Manakil project	Jun. 1960	Amortization begins June 1962	6	15·5
THAILAND	Irrigation project	Oct. 1950	1956–71	4	18·0
UNITED KINGDOM Fed. of Rhod. & Nyasaland Kenya	Development of African farming, S. Rhodesia Development of African agriculture and roads	Apr. 1960 May 1960	— —	6 6	5·6 5·6
URUGUAY	Agricultural development	Dec. 1959	1963–71	6	7·0
					$181·69

APPENDIX V

Table II summarizes the loans granted for seven principal purposes in Africa, Asia and the Western Hemisphere (mainly Latin America). Loans to Japan are not included in the figures for Asia.

TABLE II

SUMMARY OF WORLD BANK LOANS ACCORDING TO PRINCIPAL PURPOSES:
1947 TO MAY 1960

(in millions of dollars)

Head	Western Hemisphere	Africa	Asia	Total
Farm mechanization	27·1	—	—	27·1
Irrigation and flood control	22·0	15·5	70·3	107·8
Land clearance and improvement	6·1	5·0	13·8	24·9
Crop processing and storage	2·6	1·0	—	3·6
Livestock	10·8	1·0	1·0	12·8
Forestry	—	—	—	—
Development of indigenous agriculture	—	18·2	—	18·2
Former Belgian Congo 7·0 S. Rhodesia 5·6 Kenya 5·6 18·2				
	68·6	40·7	85·1	194·4

This total of about 194 million dollars loaned in support of agriculture in these countries in thirteen years is comparatively small in comparison with the 3096·2 million dollars loaned for all other aspects of development in the same continental sectors of the world: general and distribution of electric power, transportation, communications, industry, general development and reconstruction loans. (Western Hemisphere 975·7 million, Africa 801·7 million and Asia 1512·7 million.)

Bibliography

Vide p. 30. References are to population problems.

*ADRIAN, LORD (1959): Fawley lecture, Nov. 17, Univ. Southampton: "The Risks of Progress"—*vide Nature*, Feb. 13, 1960.

AMERICAN GEOGRAPHICAL SOCIETY (1959): "The World's Underdeveloped Lands", *Focus*, X (1).

BARTLETT, H. H. (1956): "Fire, primitive agriculture and grazing in the tropics", in THOMAS *et al.* (1956).

BEGUE, L. (1959): "Vegetation of Madagascar", in KEAY, R. W. J., *et al.* (1959): *Vegetation Map of Africa*, Oxford.

BENHAM, F. (1956): "The Colombo Plan and other Essays", Roy. Inst. Int. Affairs, London.

BLACK, EUGENE R. (1959A): President's Annual Address to Board of Governors of the International Bank for Reconstruction and Development; and President's comments on discussion on his Annual Report.

—— (1959B): Address of President of I.B.R.D. to the Institute of Bankers, London.

—— (1960): Address by President of I.B.R.D. to Economic and Social Council of the U.N., New York, Apr. 7.

*BURNET, SIR MACFARLANE, (1960): *New Scientist*, July 28.

*BUSH, VANNEVAR (1956): In farewell address to Carnegie Inst., Wash., 1956; *Nature*, Jan. 19, 1957.

C.C.T.A./C.S.A./F.A.O. (1959): Report on edible legumes in Africa South of Sahara.

CHAMPION, H. G. (1936): "A Preliminary Survey of the Forest Types of India and Burma", *Indian For. Rec.* (N.S.), 1 (1–286).

CHATURVEDI, M. D. (1956): In HADEN, GUEST *et al.* (1956).

CLEMENTS, F. E. (1916): "Plant Succession", Pub. 242, Carnegie Institution of Washington.

—— (1920): "Plant Indicators", Pub. 290, *ibid.*

—— (1936): *J. Ecol.*, 24 (1).

CLEMENTS, F. E. & SHELFORD, V. E. (1939): *Bio-ecology*, Wiley, New York.

COCKCROFT, SIR J., (1955): *Nature*.

COOK, L. (1939): *S. Afr. J. Sci.*

*COOK, R. C. (1956): In Symposium "Science and the Affairs of Man": Bull. of Atomic Scientists. *Nature*, Jan. 19, 1957.

CURTIS, J. T. (1956): In THOMAS *et al.* (1956), p. 939.

DU SAUTOY, P. (1958): *Community Development in Ghana*, Oxford.

F.A.O. (Food and Agriculture Organization) (1955): *World Forest Resources*.

—— (1957): Year Book XI (1) & (2).

—— (1958): Year Book XII (1) & (2).

FINCH, V. C., TREWARTHA, G. T., ROBINSON, A. H. & HAMMOND, E. H. (1957): *Physical Elements of Geography*, McGraw-Hill, New York.

FRANKEL, S. H. (1952): "Some Conceptual Aspects of International Development of Underdeveloped Territories", Princeton Univ., Essays in Int. Finance, 14.

—— (1953): *The Economic Impact on Under-developed Societies*, Oxford.

FRANKS, SIR O., (1959): Ref. *Nature*, Nov. 14.

FRASER DARLING, F. (1956): In THOMAS *et al.* (1956).

—— (1957): *The Times*, London, April 17, pp. 11–12.

FRYER, D. W. (1958): *Econ. Geogr.*, 34 (4).

GAITSKELL, A. (1959): *Gezira: A Story of Development in the Sudan*, Faber & Faber, London.

BIBLIOGRAPHY

GALPIN, E. E. (1926): *Bot. Surv. S. Africa*, 12.
GOUROU, P. (1947): *Les pays tropicaux*.
—— (1956): In THOMAS *et al.* (1956).
GREENLAND, D. J. & KOWAL, J. M. L. (1959): In *Plant and Soil*.
HADEN-GUEST, S., WRIGHT, J. K. & TECLAFF, E. M. (1956): *A World Geography of Forest Resources*, New York.
HEYWOOD, H. (1956): *Nature*, 21.
HILL, P. R. (1960): " Conservation and Drainage on the Farm: A study of a simple system of soil management to facilitate mechanized crop production in the tropics", MS. Fac. Agric., Univ. Coll., Ghana.
I.B.R.D. (International Bank for Reconstruction and Development, or World Bank) (1950): *The Basis of a Development Programme for Colombia*, Johns Hopkins Press, Baltimore.
—— (1951): *Report on Cuba*, Johns Hopkins Press, Baltimore.
—— (1951): *The Economic Development of Guatemala*, Johns Hopkins Press, Baltimore.
—— (1952): *Surinam: Recommendations for a Ten-year Development Programme*, Johns Hopkins Press, Baltimore.
—— (1953): *The Economic Development of British Guiana*, Johns Hopkins Press, Baltimore.
—— (1953): *The Economic Development of Jamaica*, Johns Hopkins Press, Baltimore.
—— (1953): *The Economic Development of Mexico*, Johns Hopkins Press, Baltimore.
—— (1953): *The Economic Development of Ceylon*, Johns Hopkins Press, Baltimore.
—— (1953): *The Economic Development of Nicaragua*, Johns Hopkins Press, Baltimore.
—— (1955): *The Economic Development of Nigeria*, Johns Hopkins Press, Baltimore.
—— (1955): *The Economic Development of Malaya*, Johns Hopkins Press, Baltimore.
—— (1956): *The Agricultural Development of Colombia* (mimeographed).
—— (1957): *The Economy of the Trust Territory of Somaliland* (mimeographed).
—— (1960A): *The World Bank in Latin America: A Summary of Activities* (mimeographed).
—— (1960B): *Statement on Loans—Mar. 31, 1960*.
I.B.R.D. & F.A.O. (1951): *The Agricultural Development of Uruguay* (mimeographed).
—— (1959): *The Agricultural Development of Peru* (mimeographed).
I.U.C.N., F.A.O., U.N.E.S.C.O. & C.S.A. (1960): Report on conservation of flora, fauna and soil in Tropical Africa; in MS. (edited WORTHINGTON, E. B. & MONOD, TH., *et al.*).
JENKINS, D. S. (1960): *Modern Government*, May–June.
KELLOGG, C. & DAVOL, F. D. (1949): I.N.E.A.C., *Ser. sci.*, 46.
KIPPING, SIR N., (1959): On "Major needs of underdeveloped lands", Federation of British Industries, Oct. 23, *vide Nature*, Nov. 14.
KÖPPEN, W. (1931): *Grundriss: der Klimakunde*, Berlin.
KÖPPEN, W. & GEIGER, R. (1930): *Handbuch der Klimatologie*.
—— (1936): *Idem.*, Vol. I (C), includes an analysis of Köppen's system.
LOXTON, R. F. (1959): "Aerial Photographic Studies in Relation to Ecological and Land-Use Surveys", MS. Univ. Coll., Ghana: Ph.D. Thesis, Univ. London.

BIBLIOGRAPHY

MEEK, G. K. (1946): *Land Law and Custom in the Colonies*, 2nd ed., 1949, Oxford.
MOYERS, W. H. (1957): *Optima*, Sept.
MYRDALL, G. (1956): *An International Economy: Problems and Prospects*, *Routledge, London*.
—— (1958): *Economic Theory and Under-developed Regions*, London.
NATIONAL ACADEMY OF SCIENCE—National Research Council (1959): *Recommendations for Strengthening Science and Technology in Selected Areas of Africa South of the Sahara*, prepared by International Co-operation Admin. (I.C.A.), Washington.
NYE, P. H. (1960): "Organic Matter and Nutrient Cycles under Moist Tropical Forest", in press: *Plant and Soil*.
NYE, P. H. & GREENLAND, D. (1960): *The Soil under Shifting Cultivation*, Commonwealth Bureau Soils, Tec. Comm. 51, Harpenden.
PEARSALL, H. H. (1957): Rept. for Fauna Preservation Soc. on Serengeti Nat. Park, Tanganyika.
PEREIRA, H. C. (1959): *Nature*, Dec. 5.
PHILLIPS, J. F. V. (JOHN) (1928A): *S. Afr. J. Sci.*, 25.
—— (1928B), *Ibid.*
—— (1930A): *J. Ecol.*, 19 (1).
—— (1930B): *S. Afr. J. Sci.*, 27.
—— (1930C): *Ecology*, 11 (4).
—— (1931): *J. Ecol.*, 19 (2).
—— (1932): "Man at the Cross-Roads" in *Our Changing World View*, Univ. Witwatersrand, Johannesburg.
—— (1934): *J. Ecol.*, 22 (2).
—— (1935A): *Idem.*, 23 (1).
—— (1935B): *Idem.*, 23 (2).
—— (1936): *J.S. Afr. Bot.*, pp. 35–44.
—— (1949): Int. Tech. Conf. on Protection of Nature, Lake Success, pp. 336–45.
—— (1953A): In I.B.R.D. Report on Ceylon.
—— (1953B): In I.B.R.D. Report on Nicaragua.
—— (1955): In I.B.R.D. Report on Malaya.
—— (1956): *Vegetatio*, VII (1).
—— (1957): In I.B.R.D. Report on Somaliland.
—— (1959A): In I.B.R.D./F.A.O. Report on Peru.
—— (1959B): *Agriculture and Ecology in Africa: A Study of Actual and Potential Development South of the Sahara*, Faber & Faber, London.
—— (1960A): "Ecology in Africa: From the Sudan to Transvaal", *Discovery*, 216.
—— (1960B): In *Basutoland, Bechuanaland and Swaziland*. Report of an Economic Survey Mission, H.M.S.O., July 1960.
—— (1960C): *Kwame Nkrumah and the Future of Africa*, Faber & Faber, London.
—— (1961): In "Report of the Committee of Inquiry into African Education, Nyasaland", MS., to be published; Govt. Pr., Zomba.
RICHARDS, P. W. (1952): *The Tropical Rain Forest*, Cambridge.
ROSE-INNES, R. (1959): "Traditional Grazing Practice on the Accra Plains", paper on the study of traditional grazing practice on the Accra Plains, in M.S. Fac. Agric., Univ. Coll., Ghana.
Vide also ROSE INNES (1961), in press: "The Behaviour of Free-grazing Cattle in the West African Tropics".
SMUTS, GEN. THE RT. HON. J. C. (1926): *Holism and Evolution*, London.
STAMP, L. DUDLEY (1953): *Our Undeveloped World*, Faber & Faber, London.

BIBLIOGRAPHY

SWYNNERTON, C. F. M. (1936): "The Tsetse Flies of East Africa", *Trans. R. Ent. Soc.*, London.

THOMAS, A. S. (1960): *Nature*, May 21.

THOMAS, W. L. (ed.) *et al.* (1956): *Man's Rôle in Changing the Face of the Earth*, Univ. Chicago Press.

*THOMPSON, WARREN S. (1959): *Population and Progress in the Far East*, Chicago and Cambridge.

THORNTHWAITE, C. W. (1933): *Geogr. Rev.*, 23.

—— (1948): *Idem.*, 38 (1).

TREASURY, HER MAJESTY'S (1960): *Assistance from the United Kingdom for Overseas Development*, Cmd. 974, H.M.S.O.

TRUMBLE, H. C. (1955): In "Economic Development of Nigeria", I.B.R.D. Rept.

TWINING, LORD (1958): *The Times*, Aug. 26, p. 9.

U.N.O. (United Nations Organization) (1958): *The Future Growth of World Population*, Dept. Ec. and Soc. Affairs, Population Study 28.

U.S.D.A.: F.A.S. (United States Department of Agriculture: Foreign Agricultural Service) (1958) *et seq.*: Sundry reports on agricultural production in Tropical and Subtropical Africa.

—— (1958): *Agricultural Geography of Latin America*, Pub. 743.

UNITED STATES GEOLOGICAL SURVEY OF LATIN AMERICA: Special release on Water Power (1948): cited by ZIMMERMAN, E. W. (1950): *World Resources and Industries*, Harper, New York.

VAN STEENIS, C. G. (1935): "Maleische Vegetatie Schetsen", *Tijdsch. ned. ardrijksk Genoot Reeks*, 2 (52).

WHYTE, R. O., MOIR, T. R. G. & COOPER, J. P. (1959): "Grasses in Agriculture", F.A.O., *Agric. Studies*, 42.

WHYTE, R. O., NILSSON-LEISSNER, G. & TRUMBLE, H. C. (1953): "Legumes in Agriculture", F.A.O., *Agric. Studies*, 21.

WICKIZER, V. D. (1960): Food Research Institute, Stanford Univ., 1 (1).

Glossary

C.C.T.A./C.S.A.	Commission de Cooperation Technique en Afrique au Sud du Sahara/Conseil Scientifique pour l'Afrique au Sud du Sahara.
D.A.G.	Development Assistance Group (United States and certain other countries: April 1961).
F.A.M.A.	Fondation pour l'Assistance Mutuelle en Afrique au Sud du Sahara.
F.A.O.	Food and Agriculture Organization.
I.B.E.D.	International Bureau of Epidemiological Disease (for Africa South of the Sahara).
I.B.R.D.	International Bank for Reconstruction and Development.
I.C.A.	International Co-operation Administration (vide U.S.O.M.).
IDA.	International Development Association.
I.F.C.	International Finance Corporation.
I.L.O.	International Labour Organization.
I.U.C.N.	International Union for the Conservation of Nature.
O.E.C.D.	Organization for Economic Co-operation and Development.
O.E.E.C.	Organization for European Economic Co-operation.
W.H.O.	World Health Organization.
W.M.O.	World Meteorological Organization.
U.N.E.S.C.O.	United Nations Education, Scientific and Cultural Organization.
U.N.O.	United Nations Organization.
U.S.D.A.: F.A.S.	United States Department of Agriculture: Foreign Agricultural Service.
U.S.O.M.	United States Overseas Mission (of I.C.A.: International Co-operation Administration).

Index

* Because *Agriculture* is referred to directly and indirectly so frequently in text and tables, no detailed index is provided.

INDEX

Cambodia, 197

Cane sugar, 72

Cassava (*Manihot*), 70, 156

Cattle, sheep, goats in Africa and Asia, special features, 114–115

C.C.T.A./C.S.A., 110, 136

Ceylon, 39, 113, 196

Champion, 188

Chaturvedi, 188

Chile, 181, 199

Classification of bioclimatic regions: Finch *et al.* and Phillips, 184 (Appendix II)

Clements, 26, 27, 62, 150

Clements and Shelford, 150

Cockroft, Sir J., 166

Cocoa, 72, 73, 75

Coconut, 72, 73

Coco-yam (*Colocasia* and *Xanthosoma*), 72

Coffee, 72, 73

Colombia, 39, 112, 113, 122, 189, 199

Colombo Plan, 167

Communications, 157–160; poverty, 50; stimulus from development of, 93

Communities, 26–27

Concepts of patterns, problems and promise, 27–28

Congo (former Belgian), 122, 192, 199, 201

Conservancy, Nature, 153–154

Conservation of soil, water and biotic balance, 137–154; conservation area committees in Southern Rhodesia, 146; major causes of spoliation of vegetation, soils and water, 139–145; of the biotic balance, 150–154; practical approaches to conservation, 145–150; vegetation, soil and water, 137–150

Cook, L., *re* fire, 104, 142

Cook, R. C., 167

Co-operation and self-help among Africans, 151

Co-operative movement, necessity for disciplining, 93

Co-operatives, agricultural, 161–162

Costa Rica, 38, 112, 189, 199

Crops: for export, poor prices, 37–40; for export not always fully harvested, 41; storage, processing and marketing, 42; production in the tropics and hotter subtropics, 70–94; why crop

production discussed apart from livestock production, 70–71; patterns of production, 71; subsistence cropping more extensive than commodity production, 71–72; low efficiency of production, 72–74, 75–78; mechanization, 80–81; diversification, 81; heavy staffing for crop production, 81–82; subsistence and export, necessity for interlinkage, 93

Cultivation: shifting, 74–75, 147; sedentary, 74, 147

Curtis, 26, 61

Cushioncraft (Hovercraft), 159

DARLING, Fraser, *re* wild life conservation and management, 27, 67, 150, 152, 153, 154

Definitions: tropics and hotter subtropics, 22–23; bioclimatic regions, 63–65

Demographic features in tropics and hotter subtropics, 31 (Table II)

Desert: defined, 64; symbols, 66

Deterioration (potential) of natural vegetation, soil and water supply in relation to bioclimatic regions, 138–139 (Table XV)

Development, agricultural and related: aiding of, 164–180; matters significant to satisfactory development, 165–177; dynamic not static, 172; conclusions regarding, 178–180; loans for agricultural and related 1947–60 by World Bank, 199–201

Development: of crop, livestock and forestry production, 25; agricultural and related—features bearing upon, 58–60; agriculture in forest regions, 47–48

Dignity of clean dirt, 53

Dioscorea (Yam), 156

Disequilibrium and equilibrium, 27, 54

Diversification: of crops, need for, 37–40 (Table III); of production, 81

Dominican Republic, 112

du Sautoy, 94

EAST Africa, British, 193

Ecology: defined, 26–27; general bases, 61–62; significance of ecological

208

INDEX

INDEX

OCCUPATIONS and ways of life, 35–37
Oceania, 51, 181
O.E.C.D., 206
O.E.E.C., 206
Organism, complex or quasi, 27
Over-protection of wild animals, 153
Overseas Development Institute, 177

PAKISTAN: East, 195, 199; West, 195, 199
Panama, 112, 189, 199
Paraguay, 181, 191, 199
Parasites, of animals, 117
Pastoralists, classes of, 99–102
Pasturage: animal production and health, 95–118; ecology and management of pasturage and browse, 95–96; ecological setting and statics of natural pasturage, 97–100; carrying capacity in forest regions, 103–104; rôle of fire in pasture management, 104; selection on ecological basis, 107; ecological successional relations basic to sound management, 107–108; irrigated, 108
Pasture and browse: conservation and management little understood, 44–45; regional features, 98–99 (Table V)
Patterns: problems and promise, 20, 27–28; other aspects of patterning, 79–80; problems 82–86; promise, 87–88; promise of tropical soils fair, 91–92; promise of crop production dependent on certain conditions, 92–94
Pearsall, 152
People, health, food and education, 30–31
Pereira, 179
Peru, 39, 122, 181, 190, 199, 200
Pests and diseases, crops and livestock, 41–42
Philippines, 198
Phillips, 23, 26, 27, 53, 55, 66, 67, 68, 86, 104, 106, 132, 142, 147, 149, 150, 151, 152, 154, 163, 174, 175, 184 (Appendix II), 185–187 (Appendix III), 188–198 (Appendix IV), 204
Political tensions, 178
Population bomb, 167
Portuguese East Africa (Moçambique), 194
Portuguese West Africa (Angola), 195

Power: absence and poverty, 51; water in tropics, 51 (Table IV)
Prestige significance of livestock, 113
Processing of products, 156–157
Professional service overseas, 176
Protozoan-induced diseases in animals, 118
Psychological approach to farmers, 89
Purpose, 21–22

RABIES, 117
Rhodesia and Nyasaland, 112, 181, 194, 201
Richards, 120
Rickettsias, 117
Rinderpest, 117
Rose Innes, 103

SARAWAK (and Brunei), 198
Savanna, wooded: defined, 63, 66; exploitation and farming, 45–47
Scope and plan of discussion, 28–29
Scrub: encroachment, 48–49, 106–107; defined, 64
Seed, better quality, benefits from use of, 92
Shifting cultivation: 46, 47–48, 123, 131, 141, 147; taungya, 46, 47, 129; milpa, 46; chena, 46; ladang, 46; chitimene, 46
Smuts, General J. C., 68, 105, 106, 137
Soils, richness of tropical exaggerated but of fair promise, 91–92
Somali Republic, 113, 193
South-West Africa, 195
Southern Rhodesia, 194
Stamp, 91
Storage, 155–156
Storey, introduction of Kikuyu grass to Peru, 108
Sub-desert; defined, 64; symbols, 66
Sudan, 192, 200
Sumatra, 197
Surinam, 190
Surveys, economic, land-use, research and others, 179
Swaziland, 195
Swynnerton, re tsetse flies, 151

TANGANYIKA, 113
Taro (Coco-yam), 72
Taungya (shifting cultivation), 46, 47, 129

211